Arranged by Stephen Clark

How often have you been watching television, listening to the radio, been at a concert, taking part in a singsong or heard the familiar music to a song, thought you knew the words, then couldn't get past the first line or so? It happens only too often to most people. This collection of 100 'well-known' songs will enable you to join in fully, so that next time . . .

All the songs have been specially arranged for easy piano and are ideal for group singing at home, in clubs, at parties and in school. In fact, wherever people gather together to enjoy themselves!

Also available:
Songs You Think You Know — Words Edition Order Ref: 16893

NOTE:
Copyright restrictions have not permitted the inclusion of the following titles in this compilation, although the lyrics are reproduced in the Words Edition:

BRIDGE OVER TROUBLED WATER, WHEN I'M SIXTY FOUR, YELLOW SUBMARINE and YESTERDAY.

First Published 1989

215-2-556

SONGS YOU *Think* YOU KNOW

SONGS YOU *Think* YOU KNOW

ANY OLD IRON?

Words and Music by CHAS COLLINS,
E A SHEPPARD and FRED TERRY

ABIDE WITH ME

TRADITIONAL

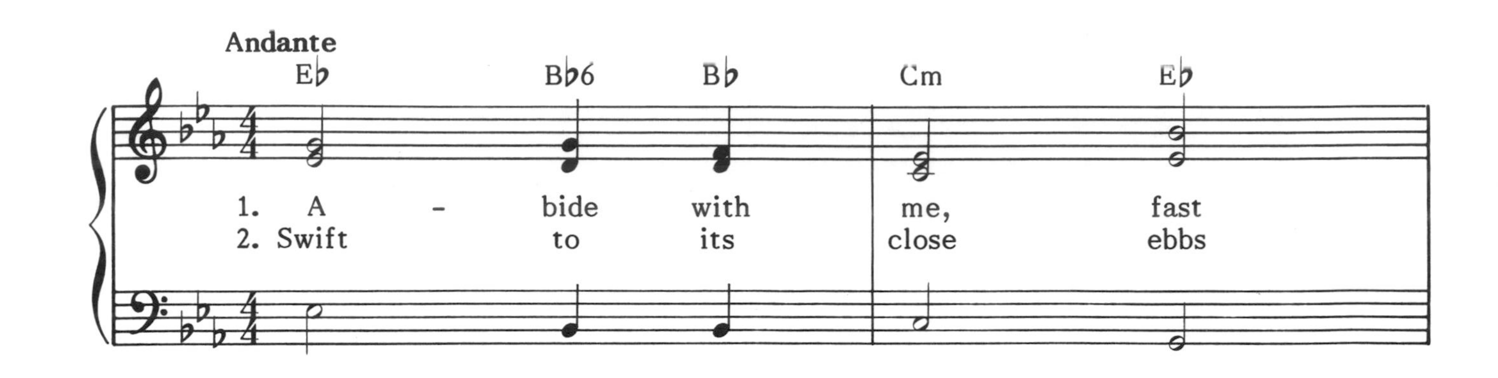

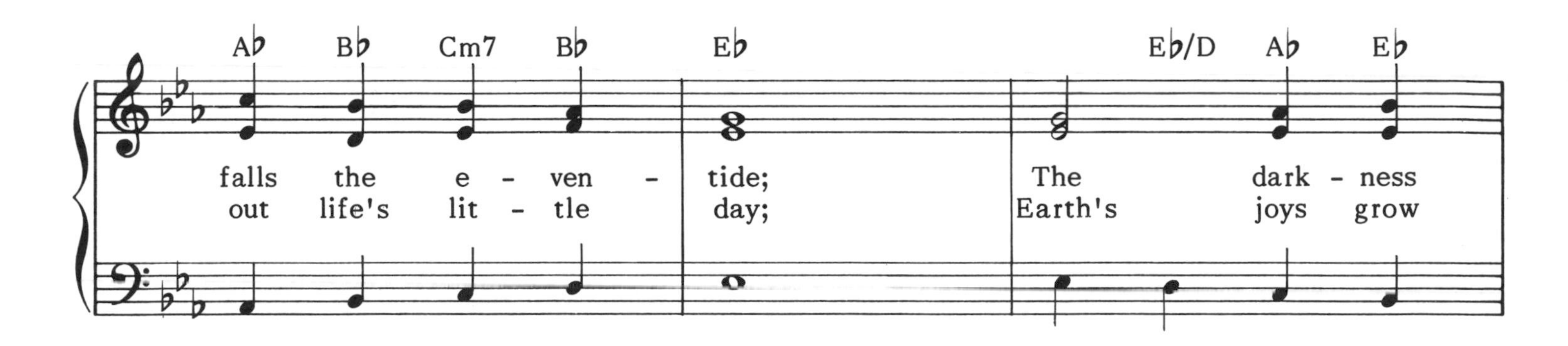

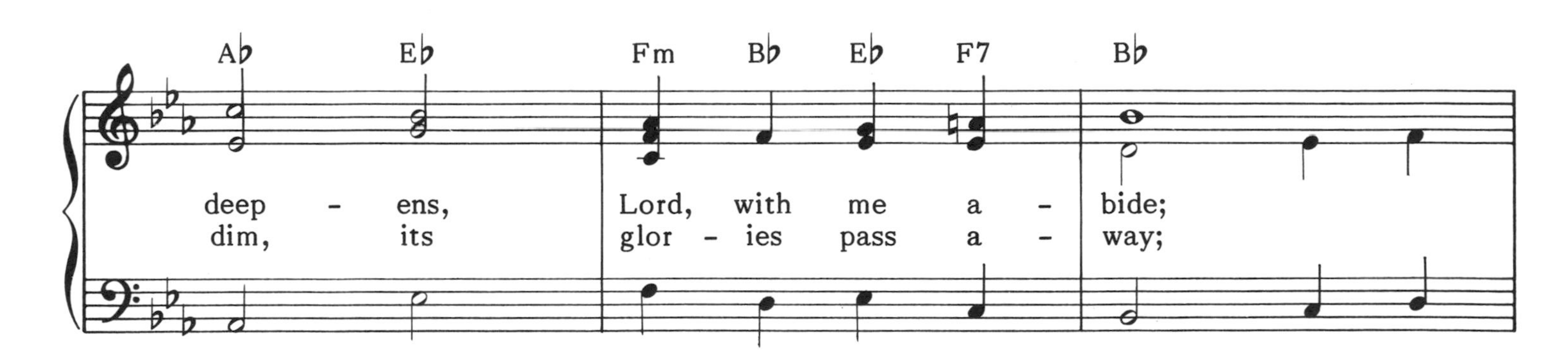

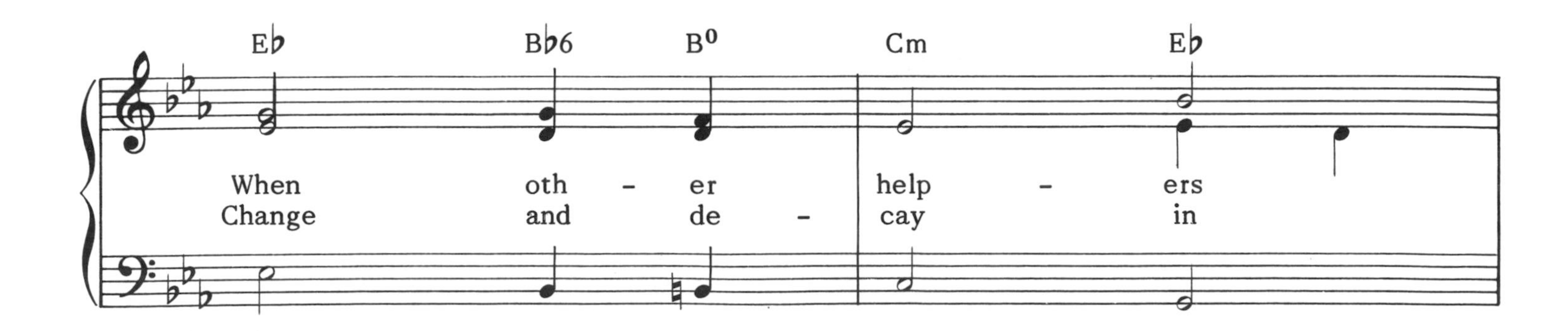

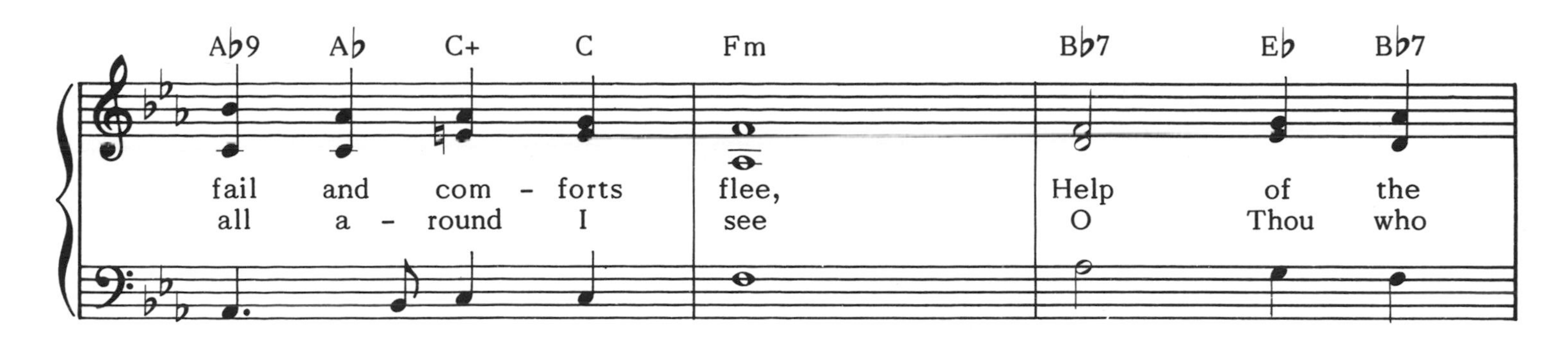

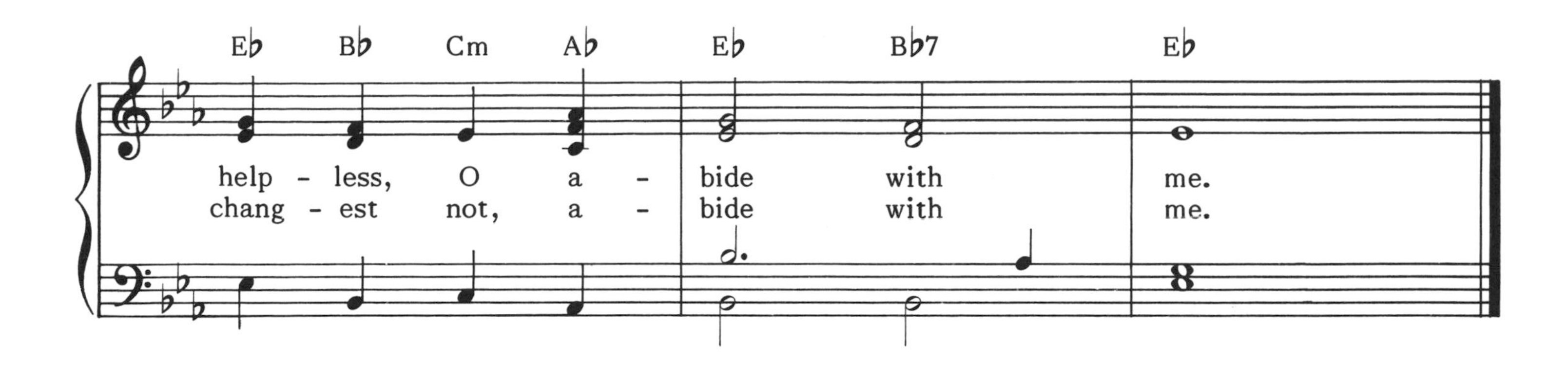

3. I need Thy presence every passing hour;
What but Thy grace can foil the tempter's power?
Who like Thyself my guide and stay can be?
Through cloud and sunshine, O abide with me.

4. I fear no foe, with Thee at hand to bless;
Ills have no weight, and tears no bitterness.
Where is death's sting? Where, grave, thy victory?
I triumph still, if Thou abide with me.

5. Reveal Thyself before my closing eyes,
Shine through the gloom, and point me to the skies;
Heaven's morning breaks, and earth's vain shadows flee -
In life, in death, O Lord, abide with me.

ALL THE NICE GIRLS (Ship Ahoy)

Words by A J MILLS
Music by BENNETT SCOTT

C
C7
sail - ors are Bright and bree - zy,
Gm C7
F
free and ea - sy, He's the lad - ies
F0
F
A7 D7
pride and joy; Falls in love with Kate and
G7
Jane, Then he's off to sea a - gain Ship a -
C
C7
F
- hoy! Ship a - hoy!

ALOUETTE

TRADITIONAL

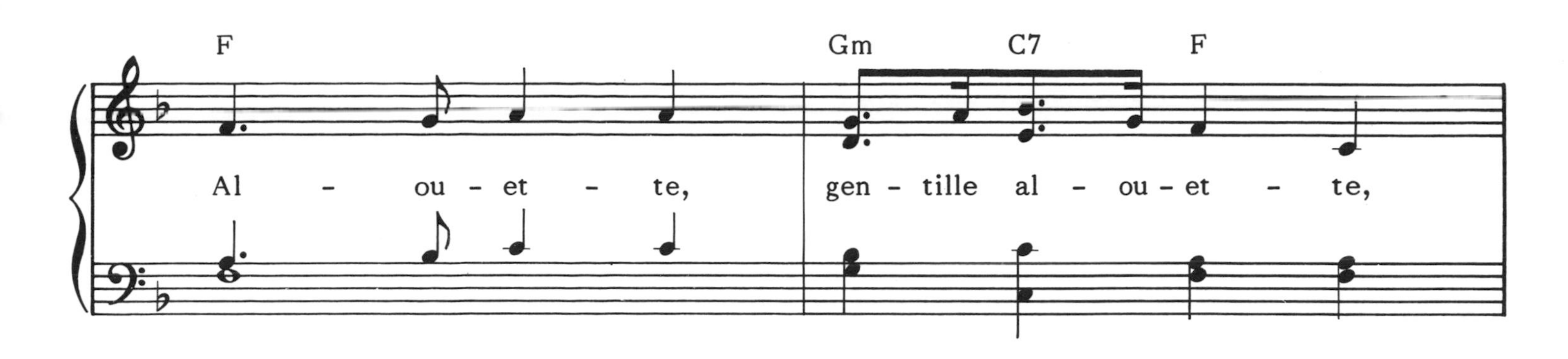

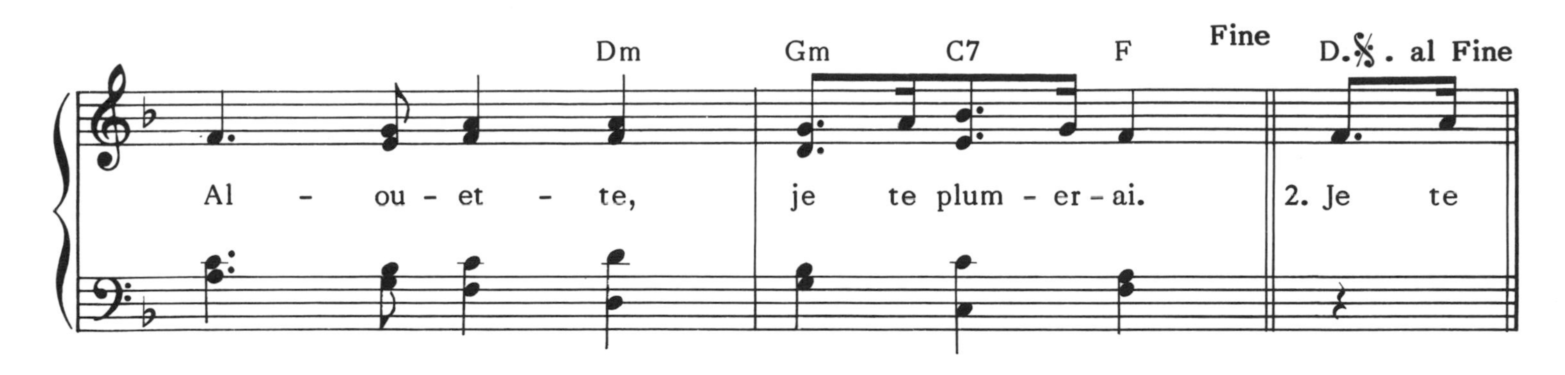

2. Je te plumerai le bec, . . .
Alouette, etc.

3. Je te plumerai le dos, . . .

4. Je te plumerai les pattes, . . .

5. Je te plumerai la falle, . . .

6. Je te plumerai la queue, . . .

AMAZING GRACE

TRADITIONAL

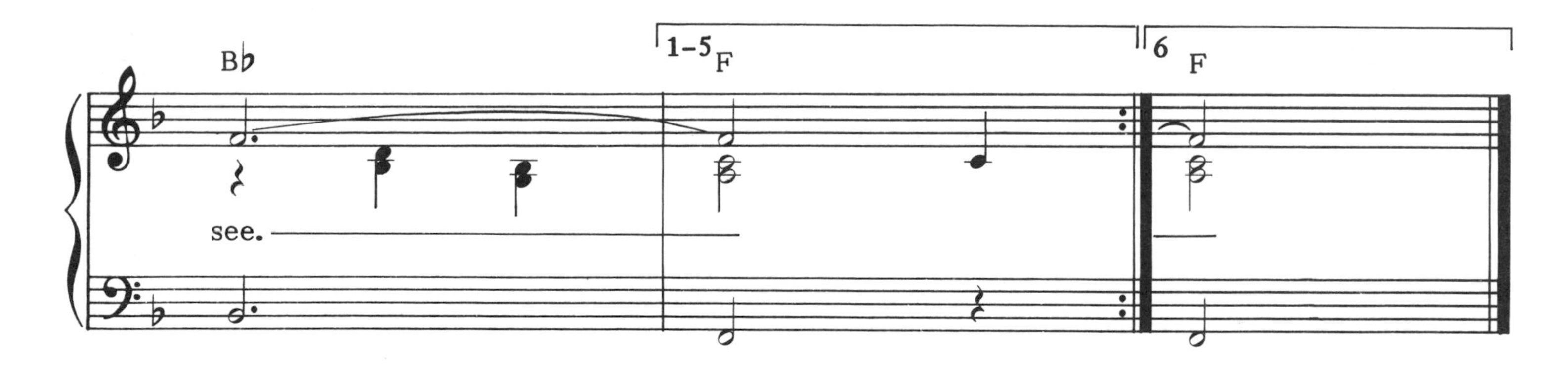

2. 'Twas grace that taught my heart to fear,
   And grace my fears relieved;
   How precious did that grace appear,
   The hour I first believed!

3. Through many dangers, toils and snares
   I have already come:
   'Tis grace that brought me safe thus far,
   And grace will lead me home.

4. The Lord has promised good to me,
   His word my hope secures;
   He will my shield and portion be
   As long as life endures.

5. Yes, when this heart and flesh shall fail,
   And mortal life shall cease,
   I shall possess within the veil
   A life of joy and peace.

6. When we've been there a thousand years,
   Bright shining as the sun,
   We've no less days to sing God's praise
   Than when we first begun.

ANNIE LAURIE

TRADITIONAL

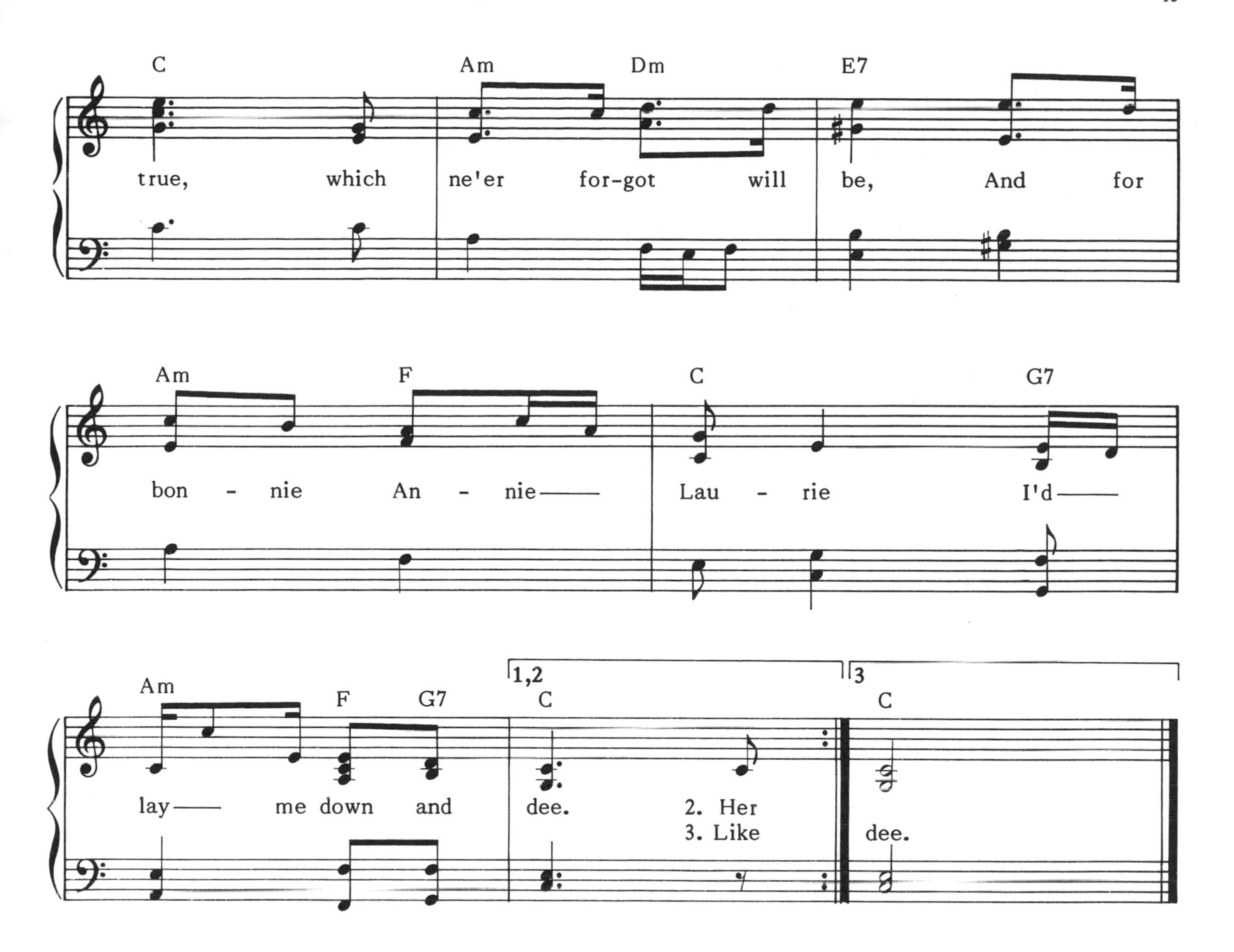

2. Her brow is like the snowdrift, her neck is like the swan;
   Her face it is the fairest that e'er the sun shone on;
   That e'er the sun shone on, and dark blue is her e'e,
   And for bonny Annie Laurie I'd lay me down and dee.

3. Like dew on the gowan lying is the fall of her fairy feet,
   And like winds in summer sighing, her voice is low and sweet;
   Her voice is low and sweet, and she's all the world to me,
   And for bonnie Annie Laurie I'd lay me down and dee.

A NIGHTINGALE SANG IN BERKELEY SQUARE

Lyric by ERIC MASCHWITZ
Music by MANNING SHERWIN

* Pronounced "Bar-klee"

Gm
Eb7
Ab
3
G7
3
Cm
Abm6
may be wrong, But I'm per-fect-ly will-ing to swear, That
Eb
Bb7
Eb7
Fm7
Eb
Cm
when you turned and smiled at me, A night-in-gale sang in
Fm
Bb7
Eb
Cm
A0
D7
Ber - k'ley Square.
G
Em
4
1
Am7
D7
The moon that ling-ered o - ver Lon - don Town, Poor
Bm7
Bb0
Am7
D7
puz - zled moon, he wore a frown,

G Em Am7 D7
How could he know we two were so in love, The
Bm7 E0 Fm7 Bb7 Eb Cm
whole darn' world seemed up - side down? The streets of town were
Gm Eb7 Ab G7 Cm Abm6
paved with stars, It was such a ro - man - tic af - fair, And
Eb Bb7 Eb7 Abm6 Eb Cm
as we kiss'd and said "good-night" A night-in-gale sang in
Fm Bb7 Eb Eb6
Ber - k'ley Square.

AULD LANG SYNE

TRADITIONAL

AUF WIEDERSEH'N SWEETHEART

Words by JOHN SEXTON and JOHN TURNER
Music by EBERHARD STORCH

C♯°
Dm7
G7
We'll kiss a - gain like
C
C♯°
G7
this a - gain, Don't let the tear
B7
C
G7
C
C7
F
drops start. With love that's true
C
Am7
I'll wait for you, Auf
RH
Dm
Fm
G7
Fm
C
Wie - der - seh'n sweet - heart.

BATTLE HYMN OF THE REPUBLIC

TRADITIONAL

D
Gm
Cm
B♭
F
B♭
B♭
- lu - ja, His truth is march-ing on. 2. In the beau-ty of the lilies Christ was
E♭
B♭
F7
born across the sea, With a glo - ry in his bos-om that transfig-ures you and me; As he
B♭
D
Gm
Cm
B♭
F
B♭
died to make men holy, let us live to make men free, His truth is marching on.
3
Chorus
B♭7
E♭
B♭
Glo - ry, glo-ry, hal - le - lu - ja, Glo - ry, glo-ry, hal - le - lu - ja,
D
Gm
Cm
B♭
F
B♭
Glo - ry, glo-ry, hal - le - lu - ja, His truth is march-ing on.

BLAYDON RACES

TRADITIONAL

2. We flew past Armstrong's factory and up to the Robin Adair,
Just gannin' down the railway bridge the bus wheel flew off there;
The lasses lost their crinolines and the veils that hide their faces,
I got two black eyes and a broken nose in gannin' to Blaydon Races.

3. When we got the wheel put on away we went again,
But them that had their noses broke they came back ower hyem;
Some went to the dispensary and some to Doctor Gibbs,
And some to the Infirmary to mend their broken ribs.

4. We flew across the Tyne Bridge right into Blaydon Town,
The bellman he was calling there, they called him Jacky Brown,
I saw him talking to some chaps and them he was persuading
To gan and see Geordie Ridley's show at the Mechanics Hall in Blaydon.

BY THE SIDE OF THE ZUYDER ZEE

Words by A J MILLS
Music by BENNETT SCOTT

F7
B♭
I've seen dia - monds in
Am - ster - dam,
Am - ster - dam,
B°
F7
Am - ster - dam,
But there's not a
B♭
F7
B♭
dia - mond as bright as those eyes By the
C7
F7
B♭
Zuy - der Zee.

BLESS 'EM ALL

Words and Music by
JIMMY HUGHES and FRANK LAKE

B♭7
E♭
G7
Cm
F7
back to their bil - lets they crawl; You'll get no pro -
C7
F7
To Coda
mo-tion this side of the o - cean So cheer up, my lads, bless 'em
B♭
F
F7
Verse
B♭
all. They say there's a troop-ship just
D♭°
F7
leav - ing Bom - bay Bound for old Blight - y shore,
Heav-i - ly la - den with time ex-pired men,

Cm
C♯°
B♭
F7
B♭
Bound for the land they a - dore. There's man-y a
sol - dier just fin-ish-ing his time, There's man - y a
D♭7
F
F7
twerp sign-ing on; You'll get no pro - mo - tion this
C
F7
side of the o - cean, So cheer up, my lads, bless 'em
B♭
D.C. al
all.
CODA
B♭
all.

CONGRATULATIONS

Words and Music by
BILL MARTIN and PHIL COULTER

D7
I want the world to know I'm hap - py as can
G
To Coda
Verse
D7
be. Who would be - lieve that I — could be
G
hap - py and con - tent - ed, I used to
D7
G
think that hap— pi-ness had - n't been in - vent - ed,
G7
E7
But that was in the bad old days be-fore I

Am
A
met you,
When I
let you
D7
walk in to my
heart.
D.𝄋 al ⊕
Con-gra-tu-
⊕ CODA
G
I want the
A
D7
world to know
I'm
hap-py as can
G
F♯ G
be.

CLEMENTINE

TRADITIONAL

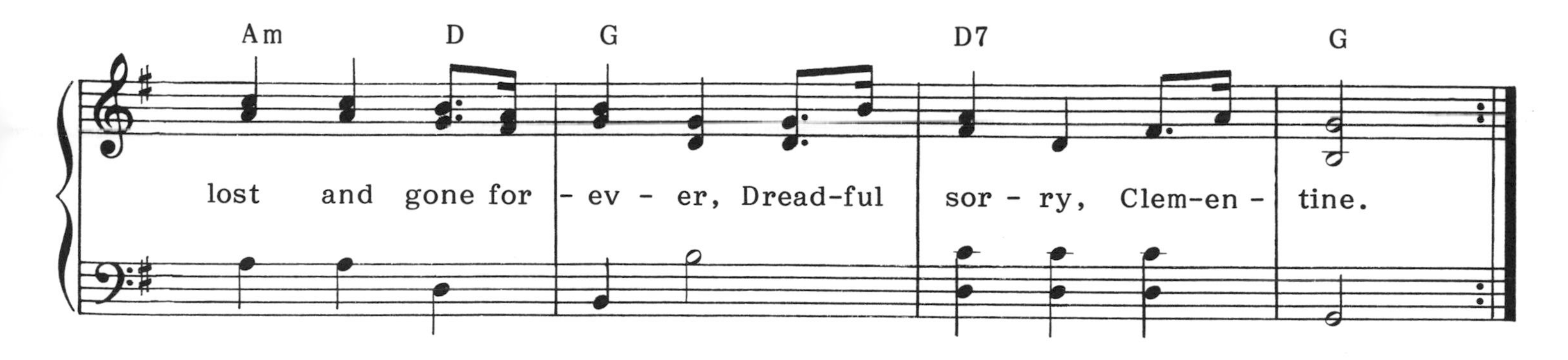

2. Light she was as any fairy,
   And her shoes were number nine,
   Herring boxes without topses,
   Sandals were for Clementine.

3. Drove she ducklings to the water
   One fine morning just at nine,
   Hit her foot against a splinter,
   Fell in to the foaming brine.

4. Rosy lips above the water
   Blowing bubbles mighty fine,
   But alas! I was no swimmer,
   So I lost my Clementine.

5. Then the miner, forty-niner,
   Soon began to peak and pine,
   Thought he ought to join his daughter,
   Now he's with his Clementine.

6. In the churchyard, near the river,
   There a myrtle doth entwine,
   With some roses and other posies,
   Springing straight from Clementine.

7. In my dreams she still doth haunt me,
   Robed in garlands soaked in brine,
   Though in life I used to hug her,
   Now she's dead, I draw the line.

8. How I missed her, how I missed her,
   How I missed my Clementine,
   But I kissed her little sister,
   And forgot my Clementine.

CLIMB EV'RY MOUNTAIN (From "The Sound of Music")

Lyrics by OSCAR HAMMERSTEIN II
Music by RICHARD RODGERS

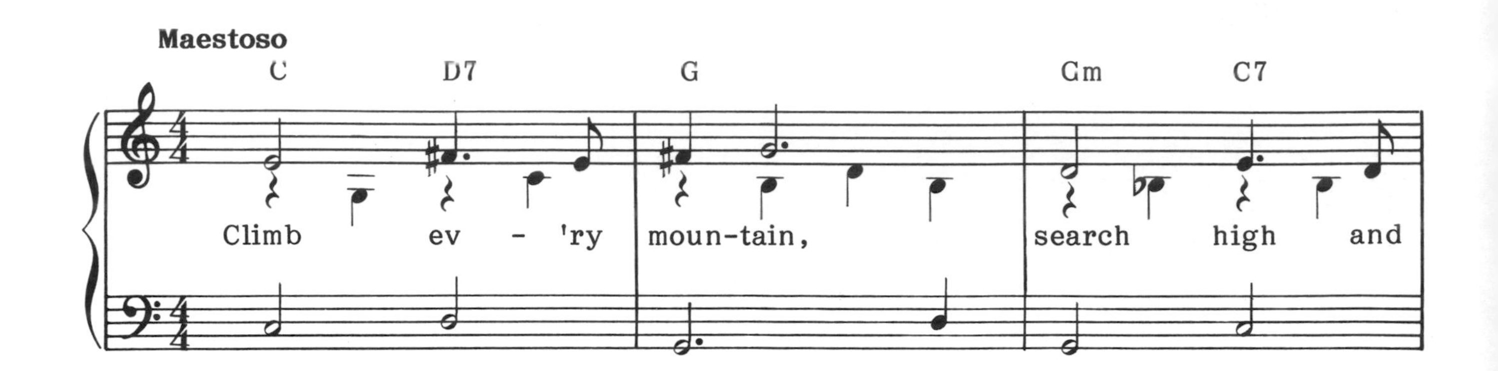

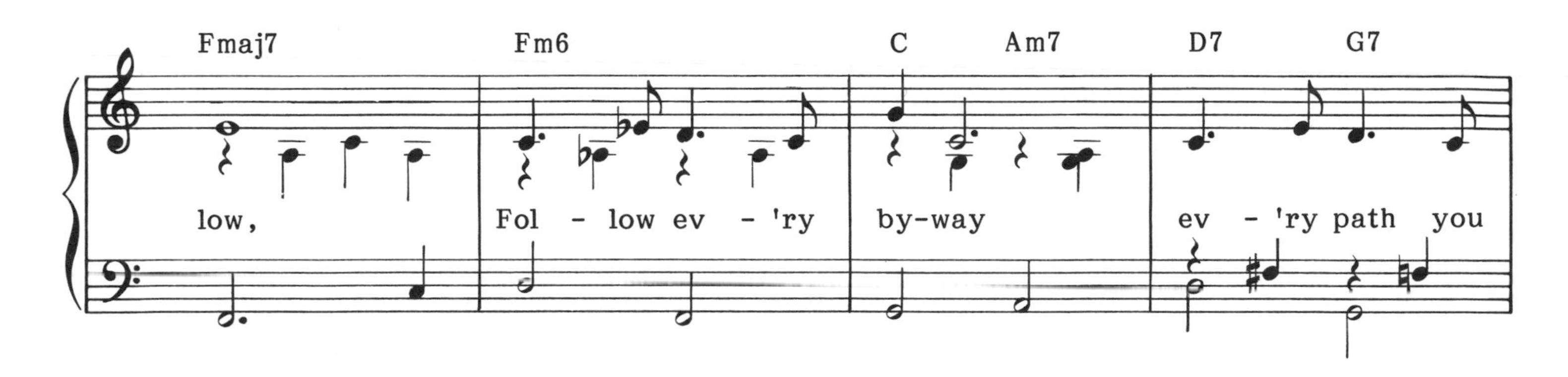

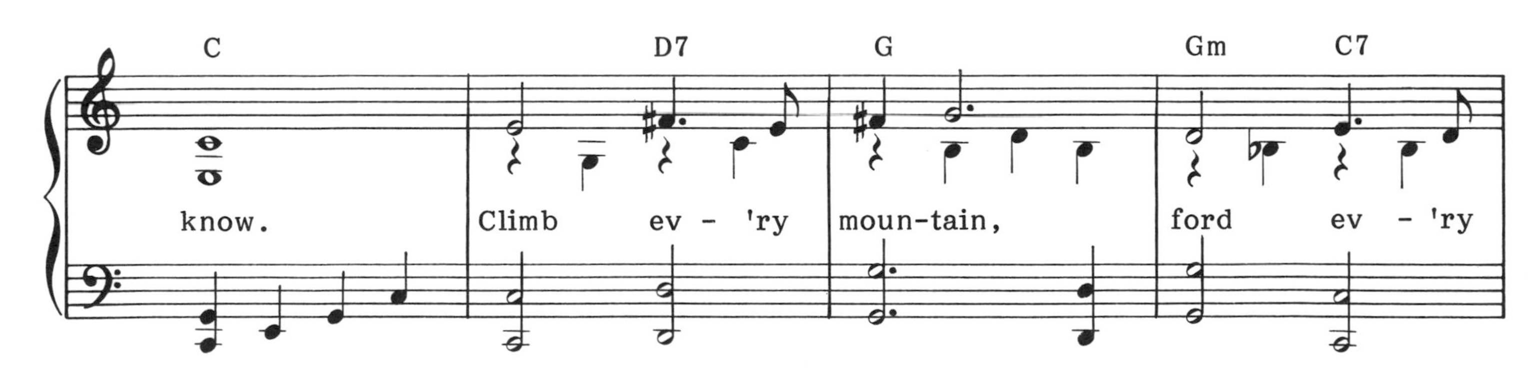

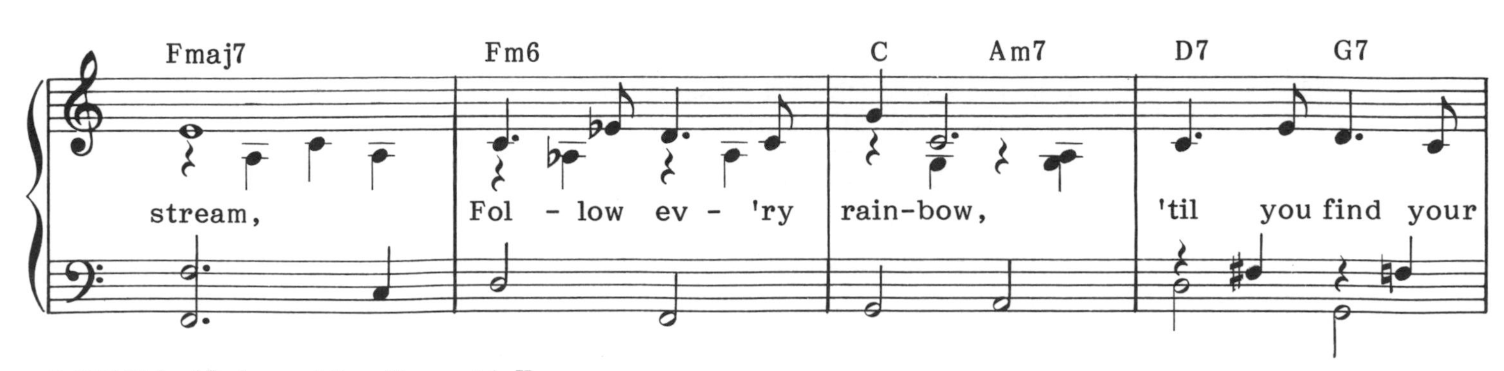

C C7 F Dm G7 C
dream. A dream that will need all the love you can give,
Am7 D7 G Em A7
Ev-'ry day of your life for as long as you
D D7 G A7 D
live. Climb ev - 'ry moun-tain,
Dm G7 Cmaj7 Am7 F6
ford ev - 'ry stream, Fol - low ev - 'ry rain-bow
C/G E7 F6 G7 A♭ Fm6 C6
'til you find your dream.

COCKLES AND MUSSELS

TRADITIONAL

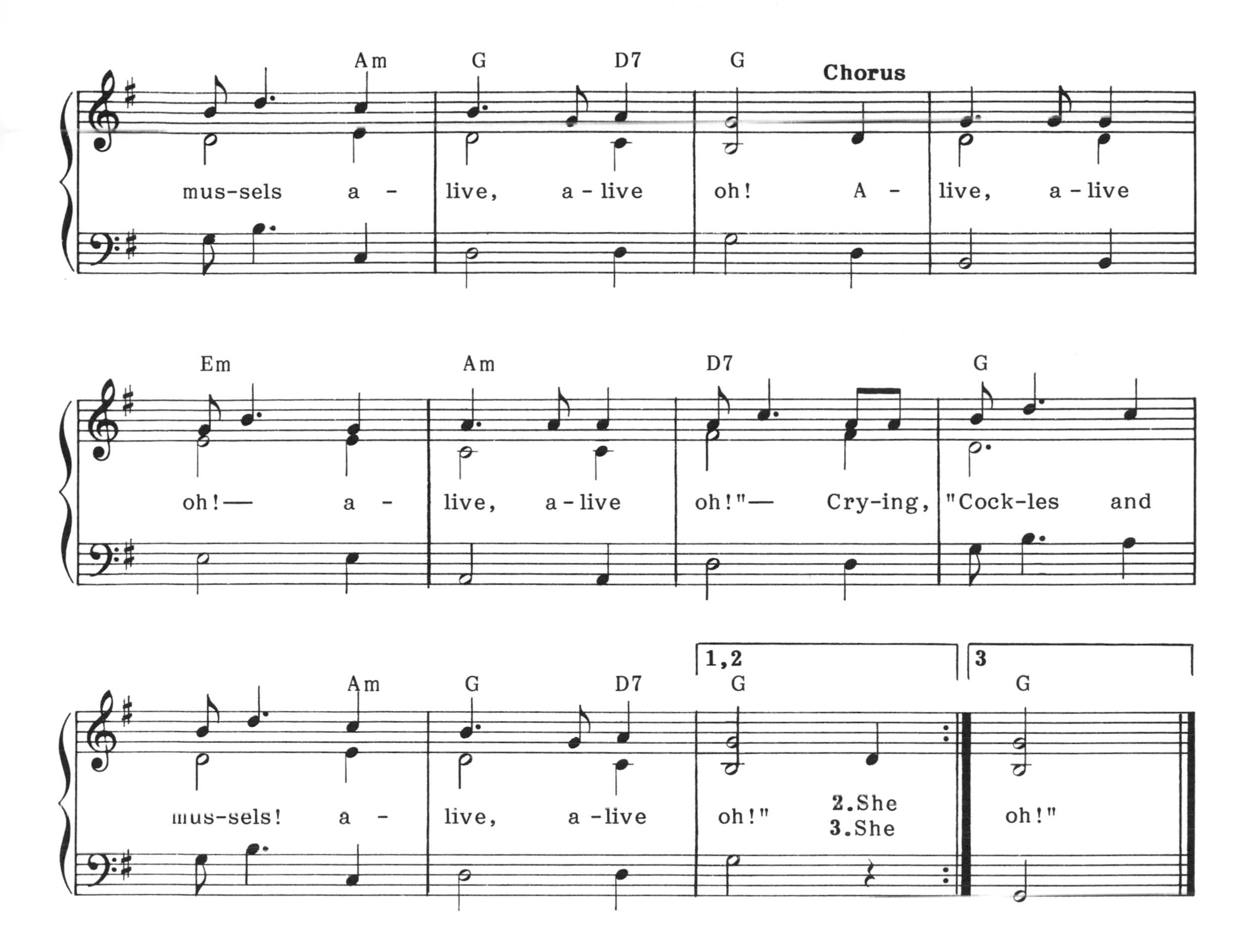

2. She was a fishmonger, but sure 'twas no wonder,
For so were her father and mother before;
And they each wheeled their barrow
Through streets broad and narrow,
Crying "Cockles and mussels, alive, alive oh!"
Chorus

3. She died of a fever, and no one could save her,
And that was the end of sweet Molly Malone;
Her ghost wheels her barrow
Through streets broad and narrow,
Crying "Cockles and mussels, alive, alive oh!"
Chorus

COME, LANDLORD, FILL THE FLOWING BOWL

TRADITIONAL

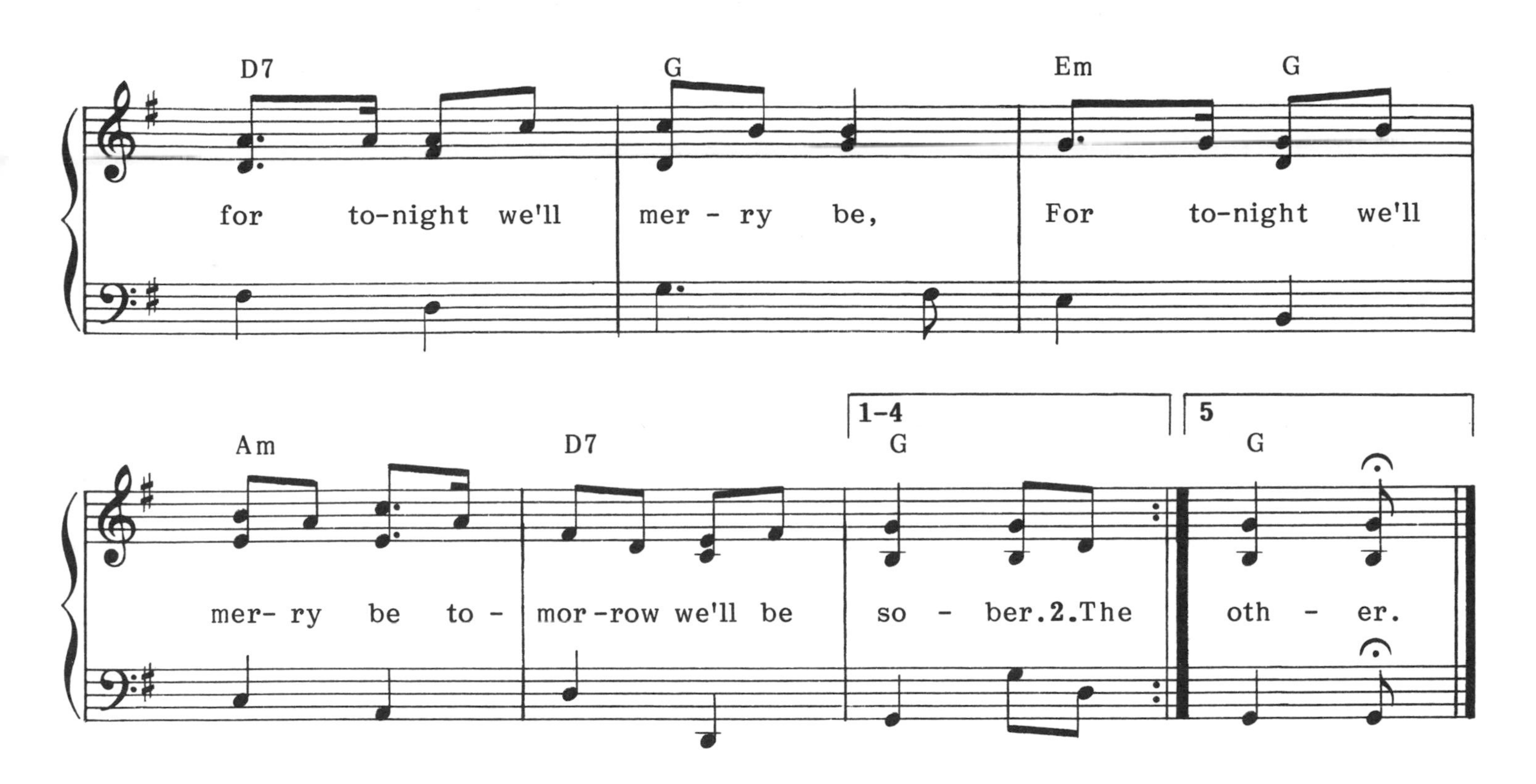

2. The man that drinketh small beer, and goes to bed quite sober,
   Fades as the leaves do fade, fades as the leaves do fade,
   Fades as the leaves do fade, that drop off in October,
   Fades as the leaves do fade, fades as the leaves do fade,
   Fades as the leaves do fade, that drop off in October.

3. The man who drinketh strong beer, and goes to bed right mellow,
   Lives as he ought to live, lives as he ought to live,
   Lives as he ought to live, and dies a jolly good fellow,
   Lives as he ought to live, lives as he ought to live,
   Lives as he ought to live, and dies a jolly good fellow.

4. But he who drinks just what he likes, and getteth half-seas over,
   Will live until he die perhaps, will live until he die perhaps,
   Will live until he die perhaps, and then lie down in clover,
   Will live until he die perhaps, will live until he die perhaps,
   Will live until he die perhaps, and then lie down in clover.

5. The man who kisses a pretty girl, and goes and tells his mother,
   Ought to have his lips cut off, ought to have his lips cut off,
   Ought to have his lips cut off, and never kiss another,
   Ought to have his lips cut off, ought to have his lips cut off,
   Ought to have his lips cut off, and never kiss another.

DAISY BELL

Words and Music
by HARRY DACRE

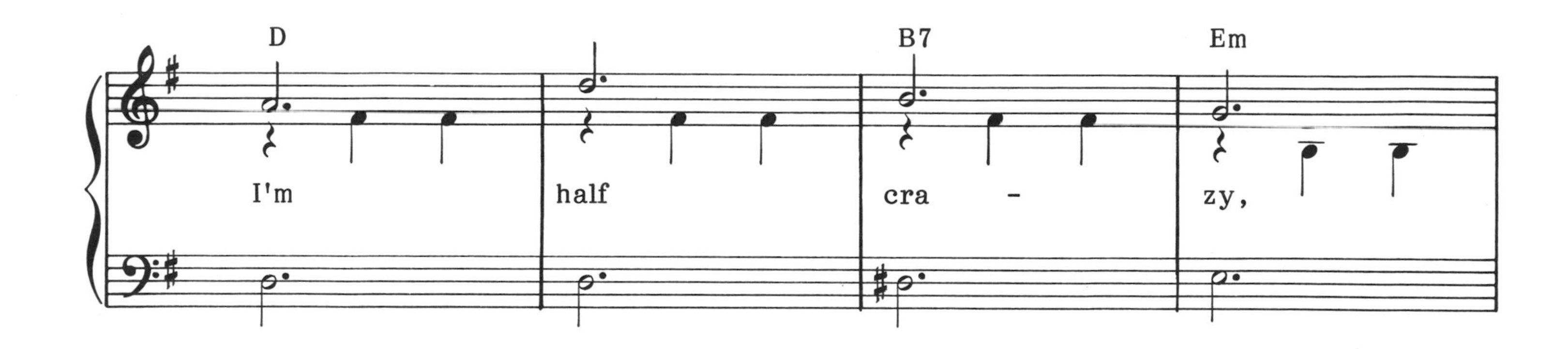

Am
Bm
It won't be a sty - lish
Em
E♭+
G
mar - riage, We can't af -
A
C
G
D7
G
ford a car - riage, But you'll look
D
G
D7
sweet, up - on the seat of a
G
Em
Am
D7
G
bi - cy - cle made for two.

DANNY BOY

TRADITIONAL

Em–
D
Bm
Em
A
D
Tis you, tis you must go and I must bide
A7
D
G
D
But come ye back when sum-mer's in the mea- dow
G
F#
Bm7
G
D
E7
Or when the val - ley's hushed and white with snow,
A
D/A
A
D
D7
G
D
For I'll be here, in sun-shine or in sha- dow
E7
Gm
D
G
Em
E♭
D
O Dan-ny boy, O Dan-ny boy I love you so.

DON'T DILLY DALLY (My Old Man)

Words by CHARLES COLLINS
Music by FRED W LEIGH

C
C7
F
F#0
C7
old cock lin - net, But I dil - lied and dal - lied,
F
F#0
C7
F
dal - lied and dil - lied, Lost me way and
G7
C
Eb7
C
F
don't know where to roam; You can't trust a
F7
Bb
D
Gm
spe - cial like the old time cop - pers And I
F
Bb
C
F
can't find my way home.

DOWN AT THE OLD BULL AND BUSH

Words by ANDREW B STERLING,
RUSSELL and PERCY KRONE
Music by HARRY VON TILZER

G7
old Bull and Bush.
C F G C
Hear the lit - tle Ger - man Band
F C G7
Just let me hold your hand, dear.
C
Do, do, come and have a drink with me
Dm7 G7 C G7 C
Down at the old Bull and Bush. (Bush, Bush.)

DRINK TO ME ONLY WITH THINE EYES

TRADITIONAL

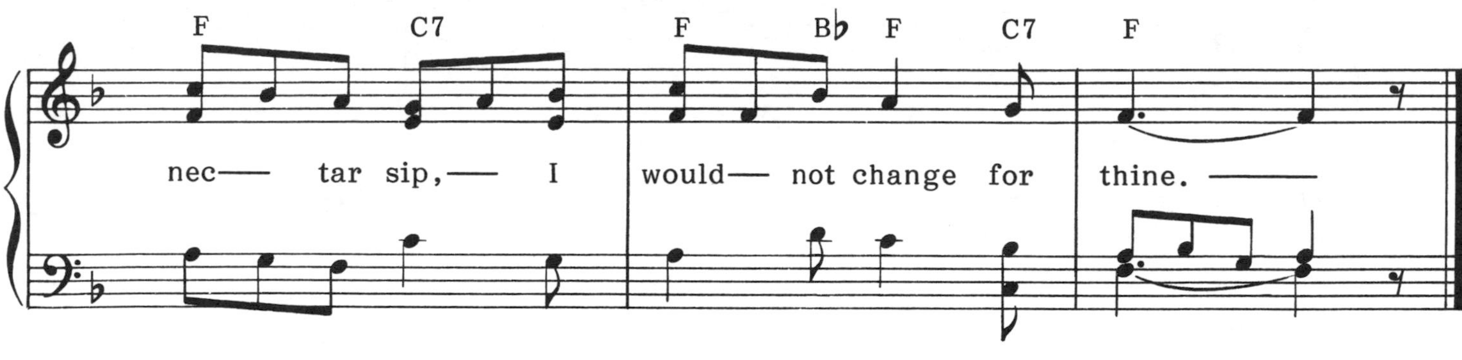

2. I sent thee late a rosy wreath,
Not so much honouring thee,
As giving it a hope that there
It could not withered be.
But thou there on didst only breathe,
And sent'st it back to me,
Since when it grows, and smells, I swear,
Not of itself but thee.

EDELWEISS (From "The Sound of Music")

Lyrics by OSCAR HAMMERSTEIN II
Music by RICHARD RODGERS

B♭
F7
meet
me.
Blos - som of
snow, may you
B♭
B♭7
E♭
bloom and
grow,
Bloom and
C7
F
F7
grow for -
ev -
er.
B♭
Fm6
E♭
E♭m
E - del -
weiss,
e - del -
weiss,
B♭
F7
B♭
bless my
home-land for -
ev -
er

FALL IN AND FOLLOW ME

Words by A J MILLS
Music by BENNETT SCOTT

D7
G7
C
er, Stand on me boys, I know
E♭m
G7
the way to go,
C
Cm C7
I'll take you for a spree,
A
A7
Dm
A7
Dm
You do as I do and you'll do right,
G7
C
Fall in and fol - low me.

FINGS AIN'T WOT THEY USED T'BE

Words and Music
by LIONEL BART

Gm C7 F7 B♭
wot they used to be. It used— to be fun,
Dad and old Mum,— Pad-dl-ing down— South - end, But now— it ain't
B♭m Am Dm Gm C7+
done, never mind chum,— Par-is is where— we spend our out-ings.
F Dm Gm7 C7 F Dm Gm7 C7
Grand - ma tries to shock—us all, Do - ing knees up rock—'n' roll,
F F♯° Gm C7 F C7 F
Fings ain't wot they used to be.

GOD BLESS THE PRINCE OF WALES

Words by GEORGE LINLEY
Music by BRINLEY RICHARDS

2. Should hostile bands or danger
E'er threaten our fair Isle,
May God's strong arm protect us,
May heaven still on us smile;
Above the throne of England
May fortune's star long shine,
And round its sacred bulwarks
The olive branches twine.
Chorus

GOD SAVE THE QUEEN

TRADITIONAL

GOOD NIGHT, LADIES!

TRADITIONAL

HELLO! HELLO! WHO'S YOUR LADY FRIEND?

Words and Music by
WORTON DAVID and BERT LEE

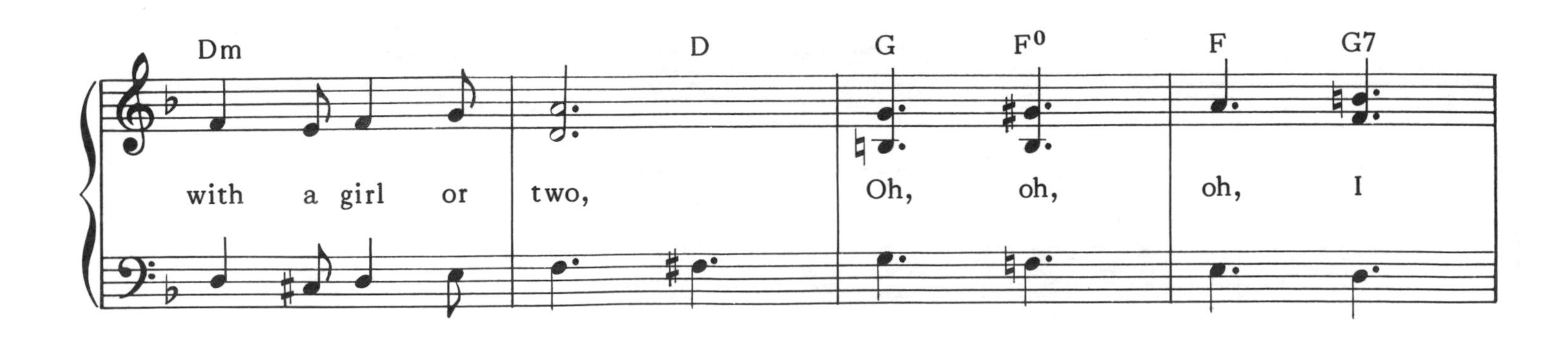

C7
am sur-prised at you. Hel - lo, hel -
F
- lo, stop your lit - tle games, Don't you think your
C7
ways you ought to mend? It
F
is-n't the girl I saw you with at Bright - on;
F0 F F0 F D Gm
Who, who, who's your la - dy friend?
C C0 C7 F

HOME ON THE RANGE

TRADITIONAL

D A7 D7 G C/G G
cloud - y or grey.
- ceed that of ours?
Chorus
G Am D7 G
Home, home on the range,
Where the
deer and the
A7
ant - e - lope
F6
play;
D7
Where
G
nev - er is heard a dis -
C
cour - ag - ing
Cm
word, And the
G/D
skies are not
D A7 D7
cloud - y or
G C/G G
grey.

HOME, SWEET HOME

TRADITIONAL

2. An exile from home, splendour dazzles in vain;
Oh, give me my lowly thatched cottage again!
The birds singing gaily, that came at my call,
Give me them and that peace of mind dearer than all.

I DO LIKE TO BE BESIDE THE SEASIDE

Words and Music by
JOHN A GLOVER-KIND

A7
D
Dm
-om - pom - pom." So just let me be be-side the
A7
D
sea - side, I'll be be - side my-self with
G B Em Em7 C♯7
glee, And there's lots of girls be -
F♯m B7
- side, I should like to be be - side, Be-side the
Em A7 D
sea - side, be-side the sea.

IF YOU WERE THE ONLY GIRL IN THE WORLD

Words by CLIFFORD GREY
Music by NAT D AYER

D
B7
E
gar - den of E - den,
just made for two,
With
A
Bm
A7
D
D♯0
A7
3
Bm
noth-ing to mar our
joy;
I would say such
F♯m
3
won-der-ful things to you,
G
Em7
There would be such
F♯m
3
F♯m7
B7
won-der-ful things to do,
If
Em7
F0
you were the on - ly
F♯m
B7+
girl in the world,
And
Em7
A7
I were the on - ly
D
G
D
boy.
R.H.

I'LL BE YOUR SWEETHEART

Words and Music
by HARRY DACRE

C7 F
val - en - tine. Blue -
Fm C7
- bells I've gath - ered,
Gm C7 F Fm C7
Keep them to be true.
F7 B Gm
When I'm a man my plan
C C7 F
will be to mar - ry you.

IN THE SHADE OF THE OLD APPLE TREE

Words by HARRY WILLIAMS
Music by EGBERT VAN ALSTYNE

Em
A7
D
G
mu - sic to me. I could hear the dull
C
Am7
G
buzz of the bee In the gar - den when
D7
G
you said to me; "With a
D
C
Fm
D7
G
C
Cm
heart that is true, I'll be wait - ing for you In the
G/D
D7
G
shade of the old ap - ple tree."

IT'S A LONG WAY TO TIPPERARY

Words and Music by
JACK JUDGE and HARRY WILLIAMS

C C7 Am C7 F7
sweet - est girl I know.
B♭ F7 B♭ B♭7
Good - bye, Pic - ca - dil - ly,
E♭ Cm D
Fare - well, Leices - ter Square, It's a
B♭ B♭⁰ B♭
long, long way to Tip - per - ar - y, But
Gm C F7 B♭
my heart's right there.

I WONDER WHO'S KISSING HER NOW

Words by HOUGH and ADAMS
Music by JOS E HOWARD

Am
Am-
D
G
D7
tell - ing
lies? I
won - der if
she's got a
G
B7
boy, The
girl who once
filled me with
C
E7
Am
joy?
Won - der if
D7
Bm7
E7
she ev - er
tells him of
me? I
Am
D7
G
won - der who's
kiss - ing her
now?

I DREAM OF JEANIE WITH THE LIGHT BROWN HAIR

Words and Music
by STEPHEN FOSTER

C G7 C
dance on her way.
fond hopes that die;
C7
Man - y were the wild notes her
Sigh - ing like the night wind and
F
mer - ry voice would pour,
sob - bing like the rain,
B♭ B0 F/C A7
Man - y were the blithe birds that
Wait - ing for the lost one that
Dm G7 C C9+
war - bled them o'er. I
comes not a - gain. I
F C7
dream of Jean - ie with the
sigh for Jean - ie with the
F Dm
light brown — hair,
light brown — hair,
G7 F/C Dm
Float - ing, like a ze - phyr, on the
Float - ing, like a ze - phyr, on the
1
G9 C7 F C9+
soft sum - mer air. 2. I
2
G9 C7 F
soft sum - mer air.

I'M TWENTY-ONE TODAY

Words and Music
by ALEC KENDAL

ISLE OF CAPRI

Words by JIMMY KENNEDY
Music by WILHELM GROSZ

sweet as a rose at the dawn - ing, But some-how
fate had - n't meant her for me, And though I
Gm7
C
Gm7
C7
sailed with the tide in the morn - ing, Still my
F/C
C7
F
F7
B♭
heart's on the Isle of Cap - ri. Summer time was near - ly
F
Gm7
C7
Fsus9
Fmaj7
F7
o - ver, Blue It - a - lian sky a - bove,

B♭ F Dm
I said, "La - dy, I'm a rov - er,
G7 C7
Can you spare a sweet word of love?" She whisp-ered
F
soft - ly, "It's best not to lin - ger," And then as
Gm7 C Gm7
I kissed her hand I could see She wore a plain gold-en ring on her
C7 F/C C7 F
fin - ger, 'Twas good - bye to the Isle of Cap - ri.

JERUSALEM

Words and Music
by HUBERT PARRY

Am Em G/D D7
coun - ten-ance di - vine Shine forth up - on our cloud-ed
G Em7 A A7
hills? And was Je - ru - sa-lem build - ed
D G D G A7 D Bm
here, A-mong those dark sa-tan - ic mills?
G G+ Em Bm G D
Bring me my
G/D G D G D Bm
bow of burn-ing— gold! Bring me my ar-rows of de -

G D Bm F♯m Bm E/D F♯m
- sire! Bring me my spear! O clouds un— fold! Bring me my
Bm7 E7 D/A A Em Am
cha - ri-ot of fire! I will not cease from men - tal
Em G/D D7 G
fight, Nor shall my sword sleep in my hand Till we have
Em7 A A7 D G D E9 A7
built Je - ru - sa - lem In Eng-land's green and plea - sant
D G/D D
land.

KNEES UP MOTHER BROWN

Words by I PAYTOR
Music by WESTON and LEE

JINGLE BELLS

TRADITIONAL

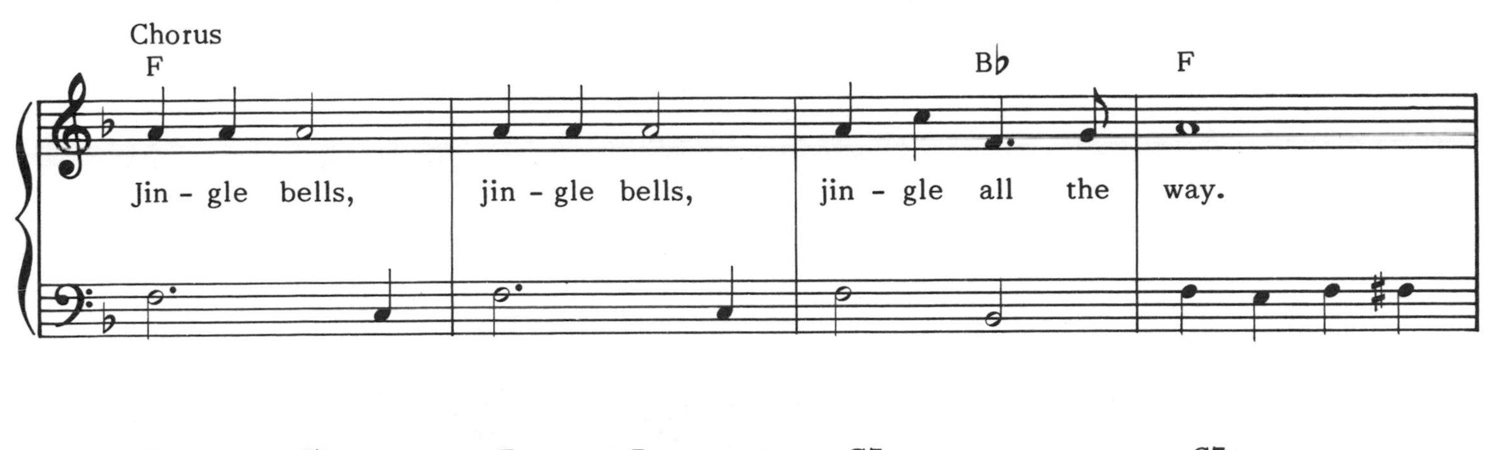

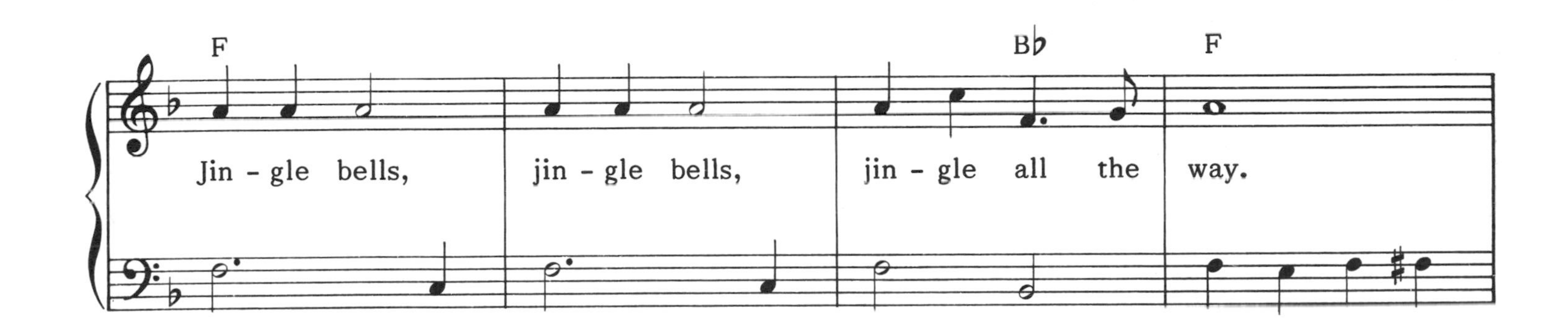

2. A day or two ago I thought I'd take a ride,
   And soon Miss Fannie Bright was seated by my side.
   The horse was lean and lank, misfortune seemed his lot,
   He got into a drifted bank, and we, we got upsot.

   Chorus.

3. Now the ground is white go it while you're young,
   Take the girls tonight, and sing this sleighing song;
   Just get a bobtailed nag, two-forty for his speed,
   Then hitch him to an open sleigh and crack, you'll take the lead.

   Chorus.

JOHN BROWNS BODY

TRADITIONAL

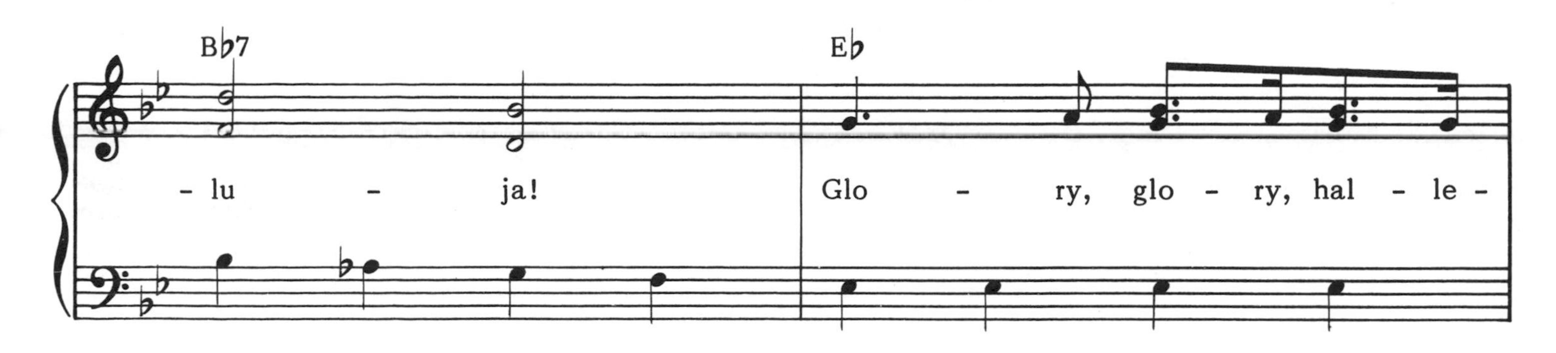

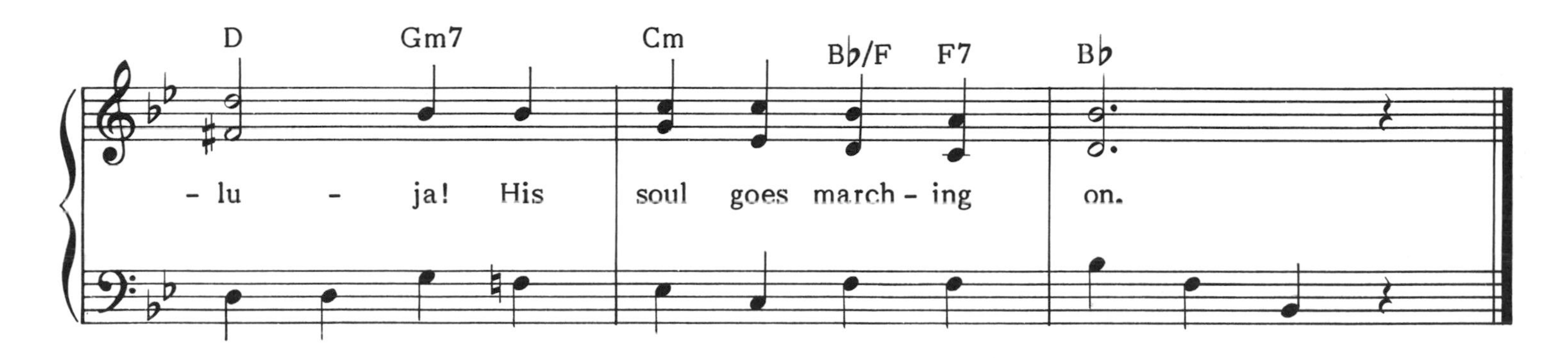

3. Now has come the glorious jubilee,
Now has come the glorious jubilee,
Now has come the glorious jubilee,
But his soul goes marching on.

LAND OF HOPE AND GLORY

Words by A C BENSON
Music by EDWARD ELGAR

B♭ F7 B♭6 B♭ E♭
Wi - der still— and wi - der shall thy
B♭/F E♭6 F7 B♭ C/B♭
bounds— be set;— God, who made— thee
F Dm7 E♭ F7
might - y, make thee might— ier
B♭ B♭7 E♭ F/E♭ B♭
yet,— God, who made— thee might -
Gm7 Cm7 F7 B♭
y, make thee might— ier yet.—

LAND OF MY FATHERS

TRADITIONAL

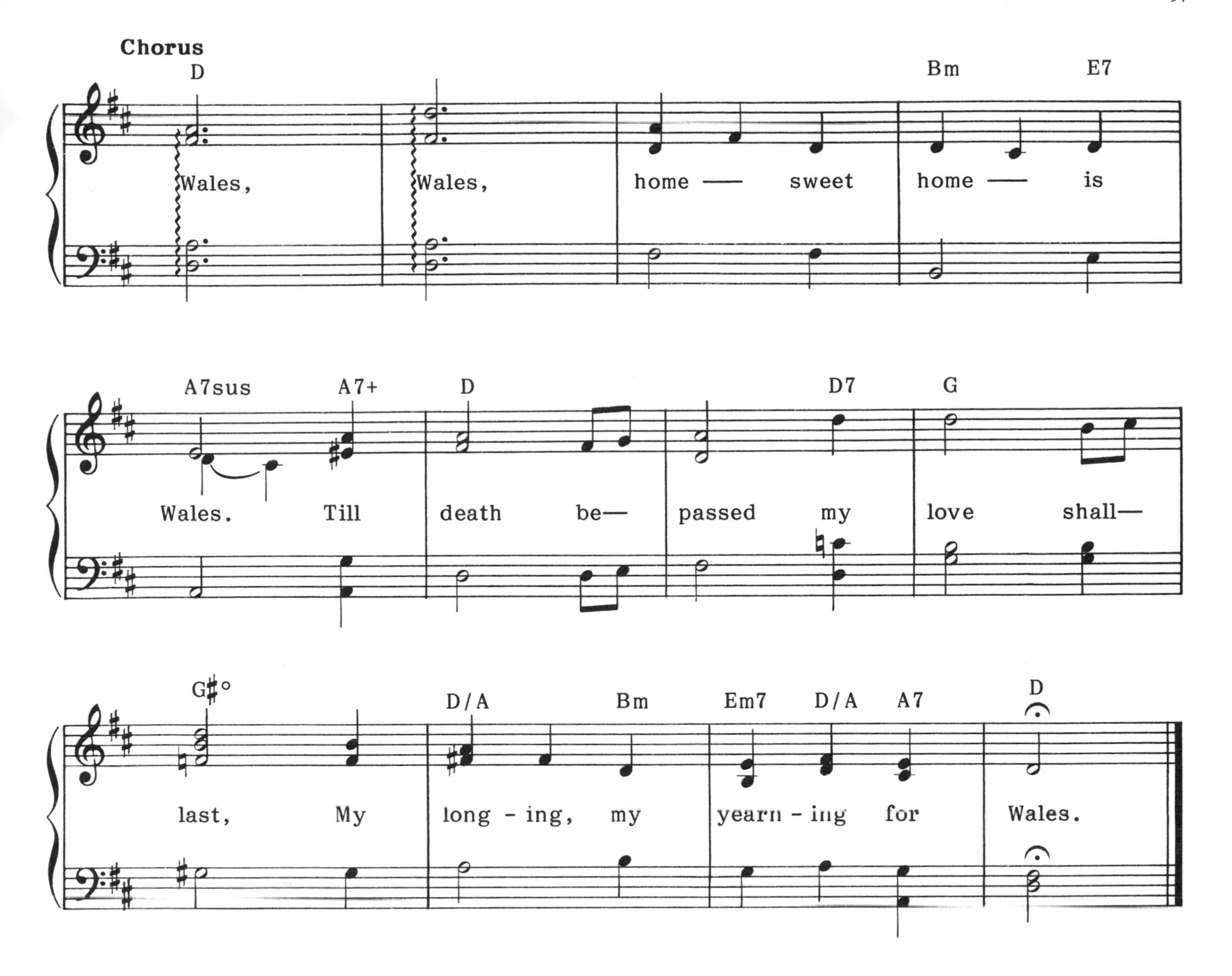

2. Thou Eden of bards, and birthplace of song,
The sons of the mountains are valiant and strong;
The voice of thy streamlets is soft to the ear,
Thy hills and thy valleys so dear.
Chorus

3. Though slighted and scorned by the proud and the strong,
The language of Cambria still charms us in song;
The genius survives, nor have envious tales
Yet silenced the harp of dear Wales.
Chorus

LILLI MARLENE

Words by TOMMIE CONNOR
Original Words by HANS LEIP
Music by NORBERT SHULTZE

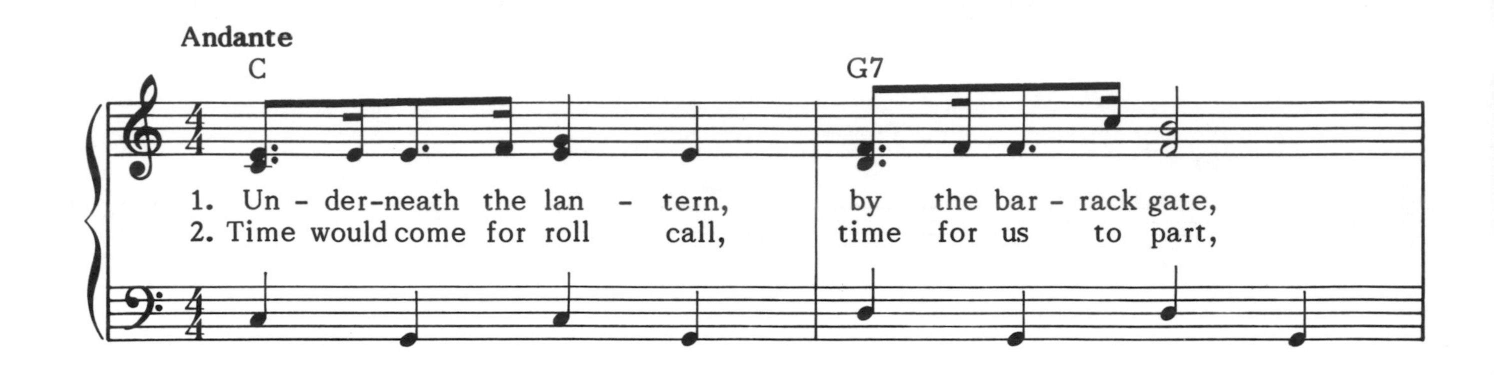

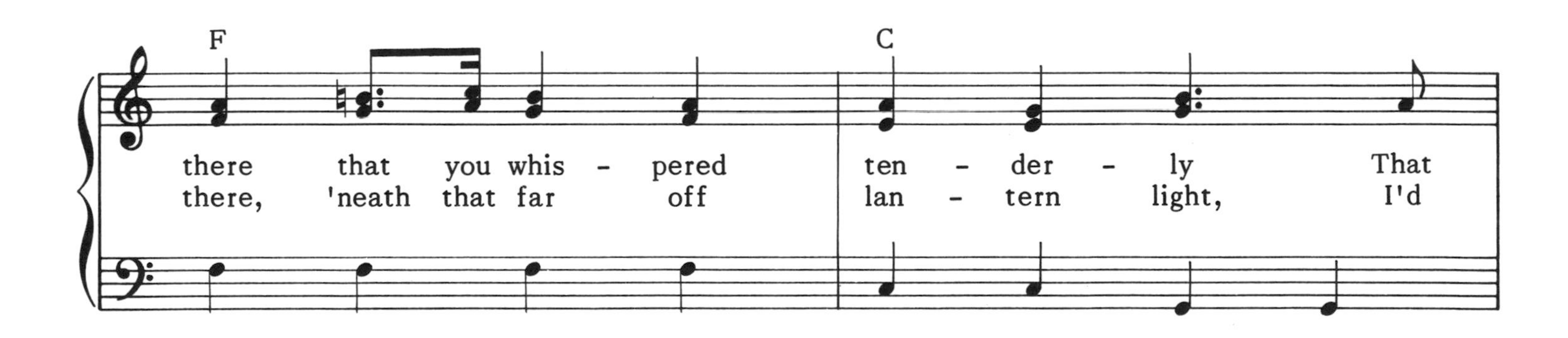

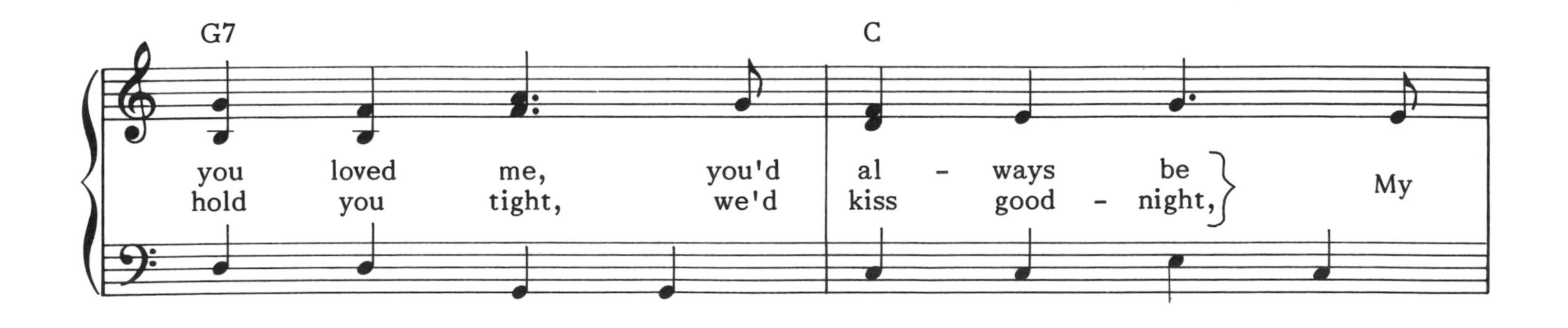

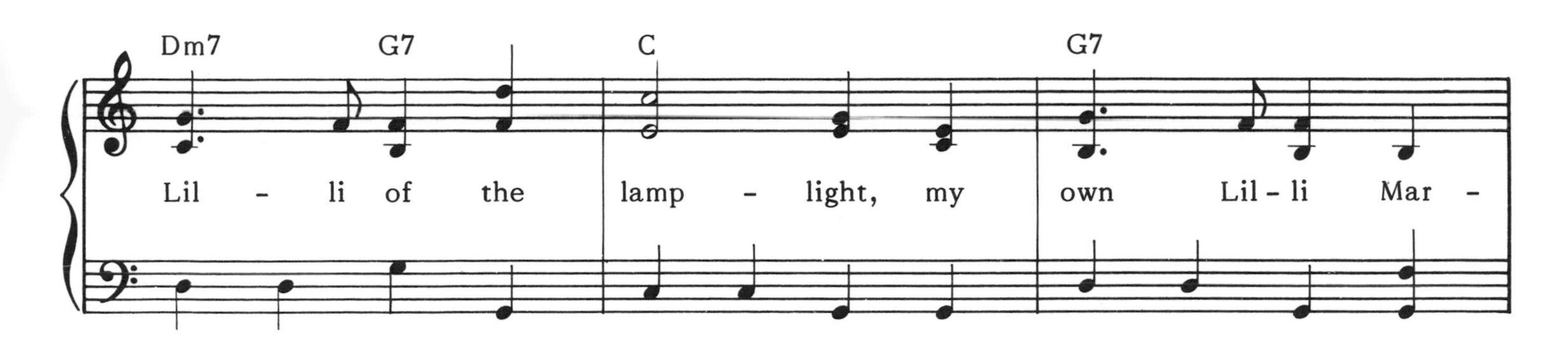

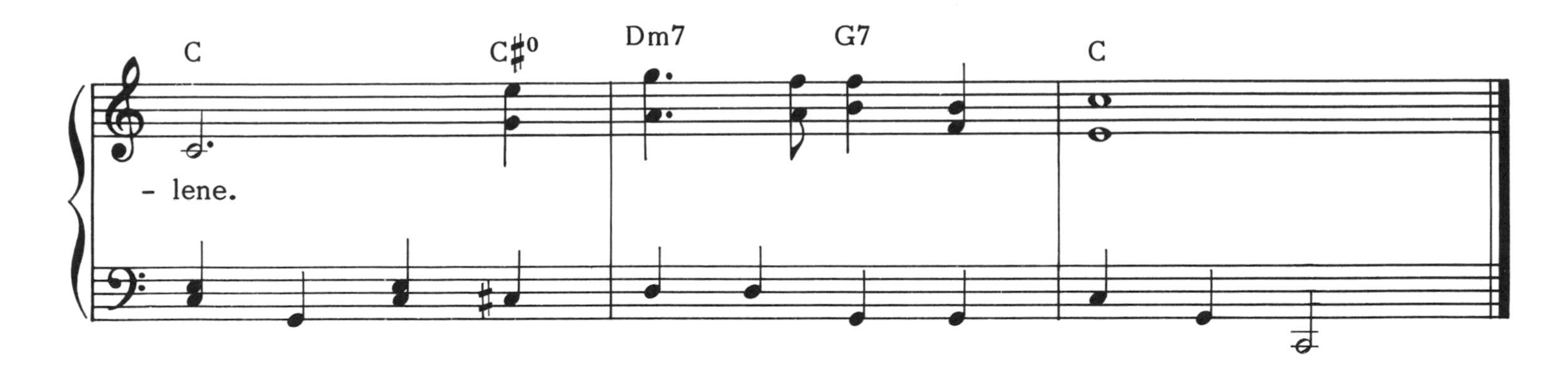

3. Orders came for sailing, somewhere over there,
   All confined to barracks was more than I could bear;
   I knew you were waiting in the street,
   I heard your feet, but could not meet
   My Lilli of the lamplight, my own Lilli Marlene.

4. Resting in a billet, just behind the line,
   Even though we're parted your lips are close to mine;
   You wait where that lantern softly gleams,
   Your sweet face seems to haunt my dreams,
   My Lilli of the lamplight, my own Lilli Marlene.

LITTLE BROWN JUG

TRADITIONAL

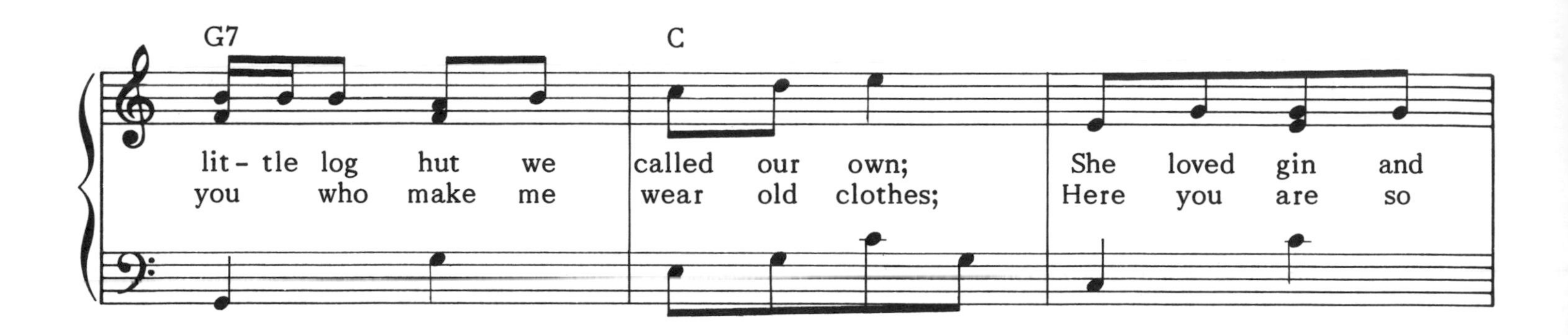

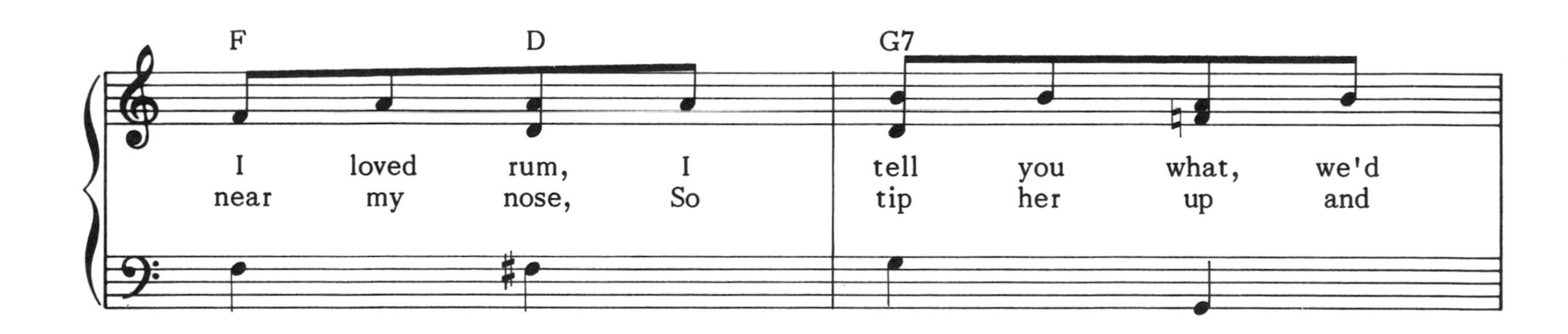

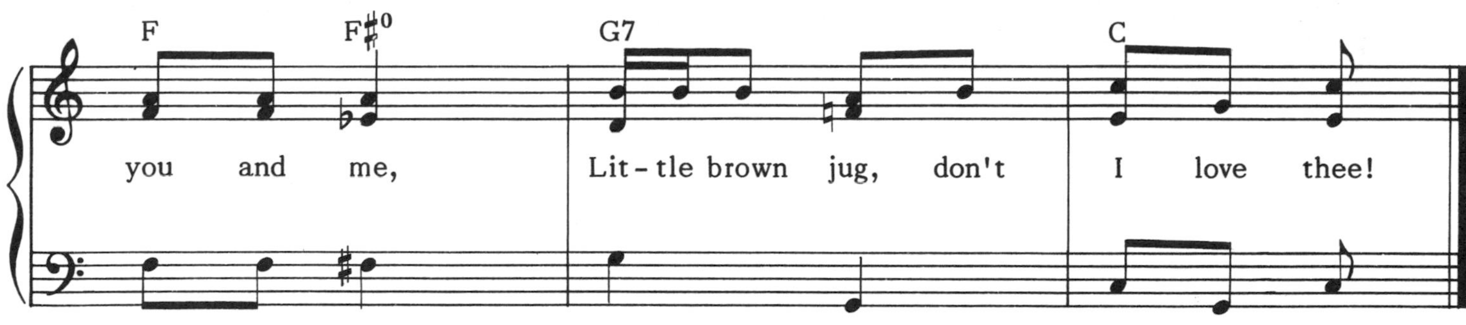

3. If I'd a cow that gave such milk,
   I'd clothe her in the finest silk;
   I'd feed her on the choicest hay,
   And milk her forty times a day.

4. The rose is red, my nose is too,
   The violet's blue, and so are you;
   And yet I guess, before I stop,
   I'd better take another drop.

LOCH LOMOND

TRADITIONAL

2. 'Twas there that we parted in yon shady glen,
On the steep, steep side of Ben Lomond,
Where in purple hue the Highland hills we view,
And the moon coming out in the gloaming.
Chorus

3. The wee birdies sing and the wild flowers spring,
And in sunshine the waters lie sleeping;
But the broken heart it kens nae second spring,
Though the waefu' may cease from their greeting.
Chorus

LONDONDERRY AIR

TRADITIONAL

G Em
gold - en daf - fo - dill ies That come with
D Bm Em A7 D
Spring to set the world a - glow.
A7 D G
O, Der - ry vale, my thoughts are ev - er
D G F♯ Bm7
turn - ing To your broad stream and
G7 D E7 A D/A A D D7
fair - y - cir - cled lea, For your green isles, my

2. In Derry vale, amid the Foyle's dark waters,
The salmon leap above the surging weir,
The sea-birds call - I still can hear them calling
In night's long streams of those so dear.
Oh, tarrying years, fly faster, even faster,
I long to see the vale beloved so well,
I long to know that I am not forgotten,
And there at home in peace to dwell.

MACNAMARA'S BAND

Words by JOHN J STAMFORD
Music by SHAMUS O'CONNOR

Chorus
G C D7 G D7
si - cian-ers you hear a - bout to - day.
jus - tice like old Mac - na - ma - ra's band.
When the
G D7 G
drums go bang, the cym - bals clang, the horns will blaze a - way Mac -
D7 G Em A7 D7
Car - thy puffs the old bas-soon while Doyle the pipes will play, Oh,
G D7 G
Hennessy Tennessy too-tles the flute, my word 'tis some-thing grand, Oh, a
D7 G C D7 G
cred - it to old Ire - land, boys, is Mac - na-ma - ra's band. Tra-la - la

3. We play at wakes and weddings, and at ev'ry county ball,
And at any great man's funeral we play the "Dead March in Saul."
When the Prince of Wales to Ireland came, he shook me by the hand,
And said he'd never heard the like of Macnamara's band.
Chorus

MADEMOISELLE FROM ARMENTIERES

Words and Music by
HARRY CARLTON and J A TUNBRIDGE

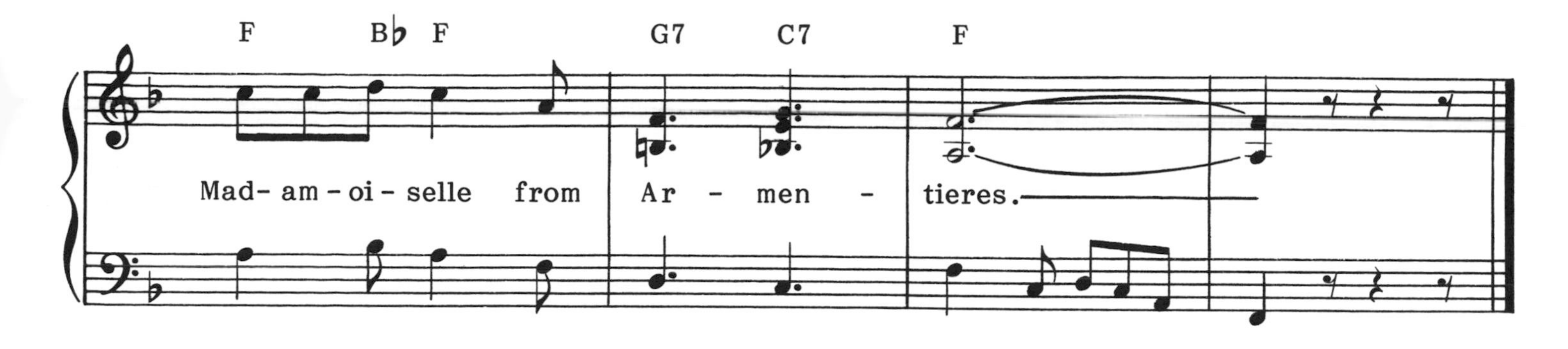

2. Madamoiselle from armentieres, Parlez-vous?
Madamoiselle from Armentieres, Same to you.
Who was it pinched the barber's pole,
And used it for fuel to save the coal?
Madamoiselle from Armentieres.

3. Madamoiselle from Armentieres, Parlez-vous?
Madamoiselle from Armentieres, Same to you.
Who was it tied his kilt with string,
To stop it from doing the highland fling?
Madamoiselle from Armentieres.

MARY'S A GRAND OLD NAME

Words and Music
by GEORGE M COHAN

MAYBE IT'S BECAUSE I'M A LONDONER

Words and Music
by HUBERT GREGG

MEN OF HARLECH

TRADITIONAL

2. 'Tis the tramp of Saxon foemen,
Saxon spearmen, Saxon bowmen,
Be they knights, or hinds or yeomen,
They shall bite the ground.
Chorus

MICHAEL ROW THE BOAT

TRADITIONAL

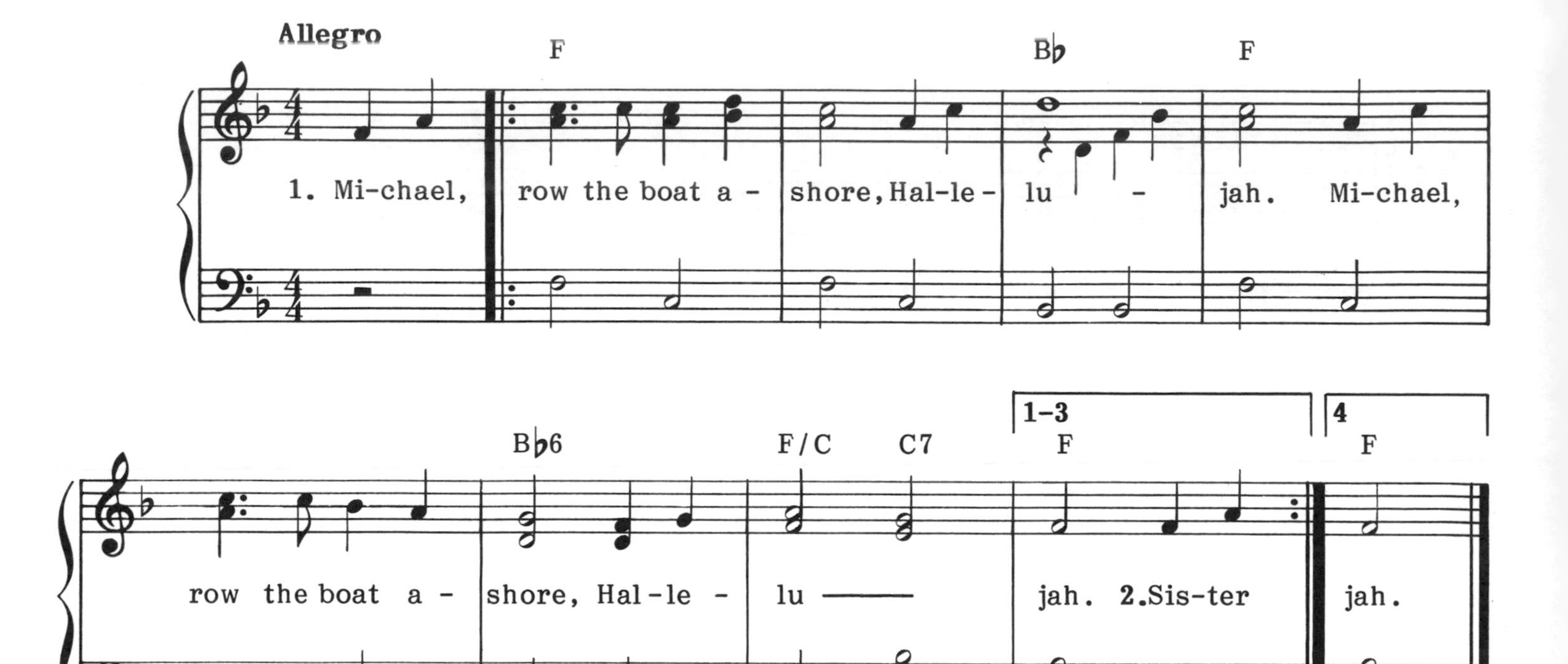

2. Sister, help to trim the sail,
   Hallelujah.
   Sister, help to trim the sail,
   Hallelujah.

3. Brother, won't you give a hand,
   Hallelujah.
   Brother, won't you give a hand,
   Hallelujah.

4. Jordan's deep and Jordan's wide,
   Hallelujah.
   Jordan's deep and Jordan's wide,
   Hallelujah.

MY GRANDFATHER'S CLOCK

TRADITIONAL

Bm7
Em
Am
D
bought on the morn of the day that he was born, And was
Bm7
Em
Am7
D7
al - ways his trea - sure and pride; But it
G
D
G7
C
Am
stopped short, nev-er to go a - gain When the
Chorus
G/D
D7
G
D
G
C G
old man died. Nine-ty years with-out slumber-ing,
D
G
C G
Tick, tock, tick, tock, His life sec- onds num-ber - ing,

2. In watching its pendulum swing to and fro,
Many hours he spent while a boy;
And in childhood and manhood the clock seemed to know
And to share both his grief and his joy.
For it struck twenty-four when he entered at the door
With a blooming and beautiful bride;
But it stopped short, never to go again
When the old man died.
Chorus

3. My grandfather said of those that he could hire,
Not a servant so faithful he found;
For it wasted no time and had but one desire
At the close of each week to be wound.
And it kept in its place, not a frown upon its face,
And its hands never hung by its side;
But it stopped short, never to go again
When the old man died.
Chorus

MY BONNIE

TRADITIONAL

2. Last night as I lay on my pillow,
Last night as I lay on my bed,
Last night as I lay on my pillow,
I dreamed that my Bonnie was dead.
Chorus

3. The winds have blown over the ocean,
The winds have blown over the sea,
The winds have blown over the ocean
And brought back my Bonnie to me.
Chorus

MY OLD DUTCH

Words by A C INGLE
Music by C ALBERT CHEVALIER

D
Em A7 D
been to - geth - er now for for - ty years, And it
Bm E7 A
Bm C♯
don't seem a day too much, There ain't a la - dy liv - in'
F♯m F♯/E Bm/D B Em D/A A7
in the land As I'd swap for my dear old
D Dm A Bm C♯
Dutch, There ain't a la - dy liv - in'
F♯m F♯/E Bm/D B Em D/A A7 D
in the land As I'd swap for my dear old Dutch.

NOW IS THE HOUR (Haere Ra)

Words and Music by
CLEMENT SCOTT and MAENA KAIHAU

Dsus D7 G C D7
sea. While you're a -
G D7
- way, Oh please re -
G C
- mem - ber me, When
C6 C#0 G/D E7
you re - turn you'll find me
A7 D7 G
wait - ing here.

NELLIE DEAN

Words and Music
by HARRY ARMSTRONG

O GOD OUR HELP IN AGES PAST

Words by I WATTS
Music by W CROFT

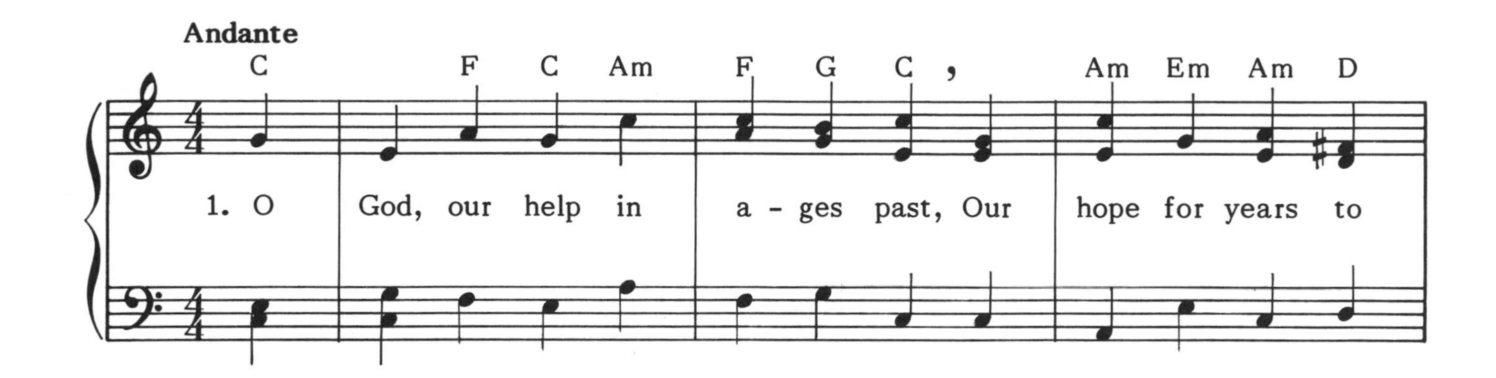

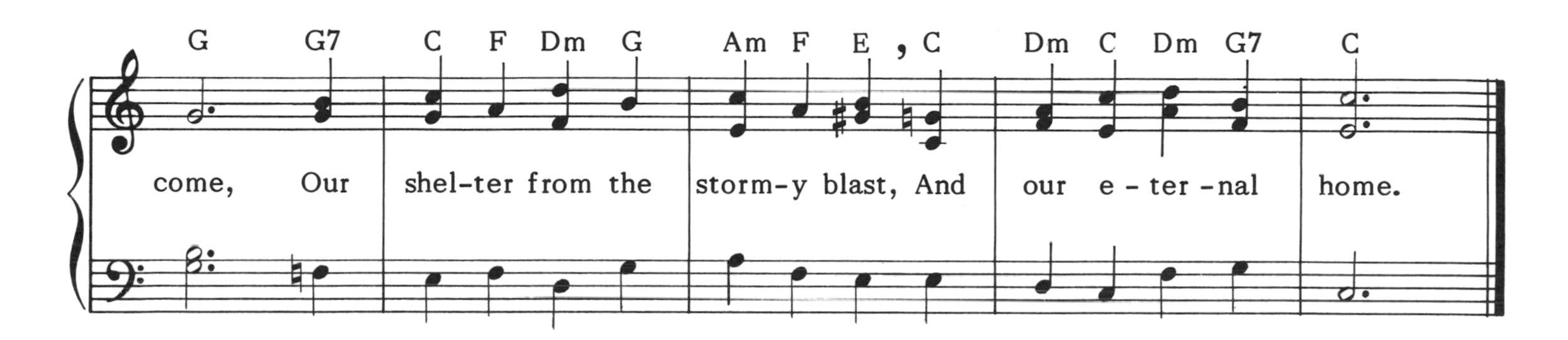

2. Under the shadow of Thy throne
Thy saints have dwelt secure;
Sufficient is Thine arm alone,
And our defence is sure.

3. Before the hills in order stood,
Or earth received her frame,
From everlasting Thou art God,
To endless years the same.

4. A thousand ages in Thy sight
Are like an evening gone,
Short as the watch that ends the night
Before the rising sun.

5. Time, like an ever-rolling stream,
Beats all its sons away;
They fly forgotten, as a dream
Dies at the opening day.

6. O God, our help in ages past,
Our hope for years to come,
Be Thou our guard while troubles last,
And our eternal home.

OH, SUSANNA

TRADITIONAL

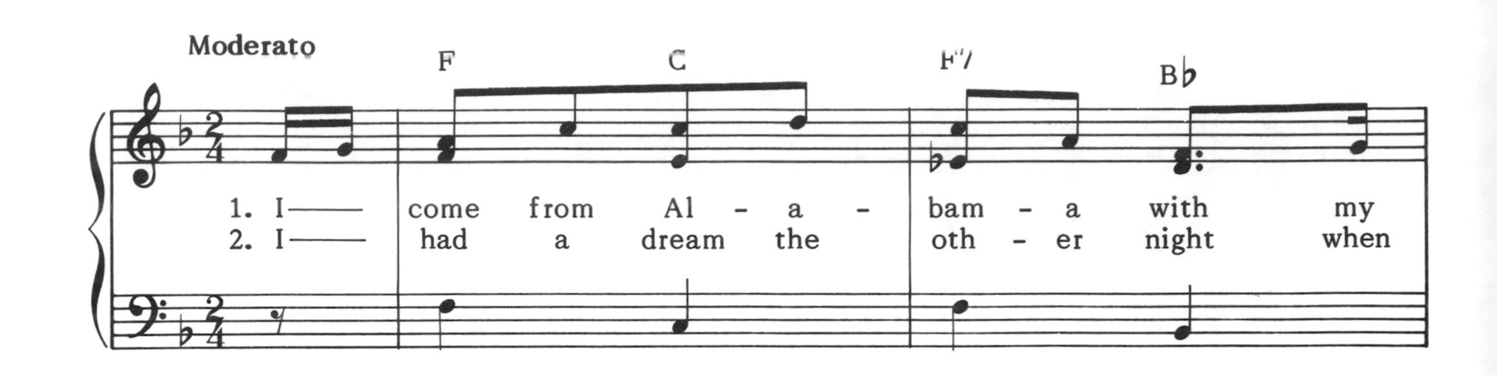

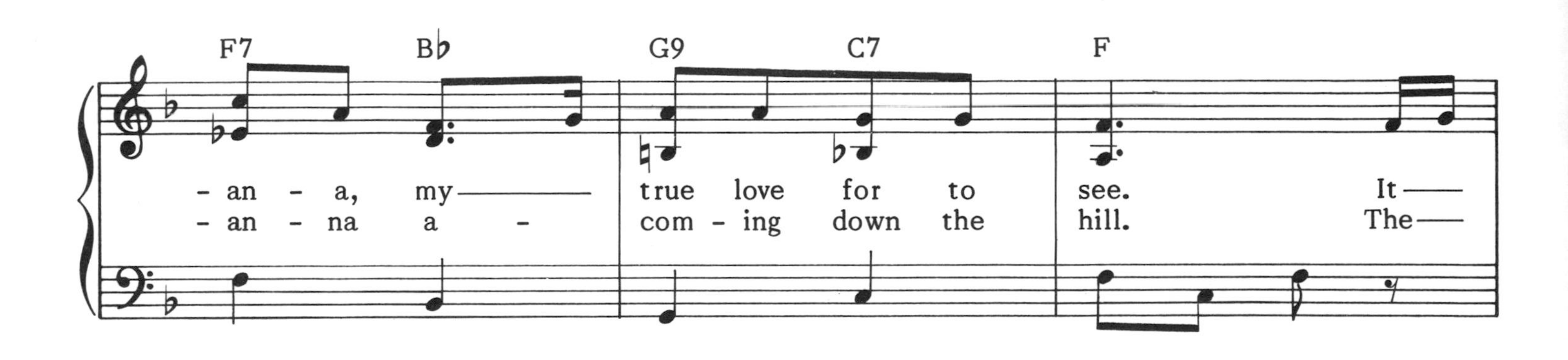

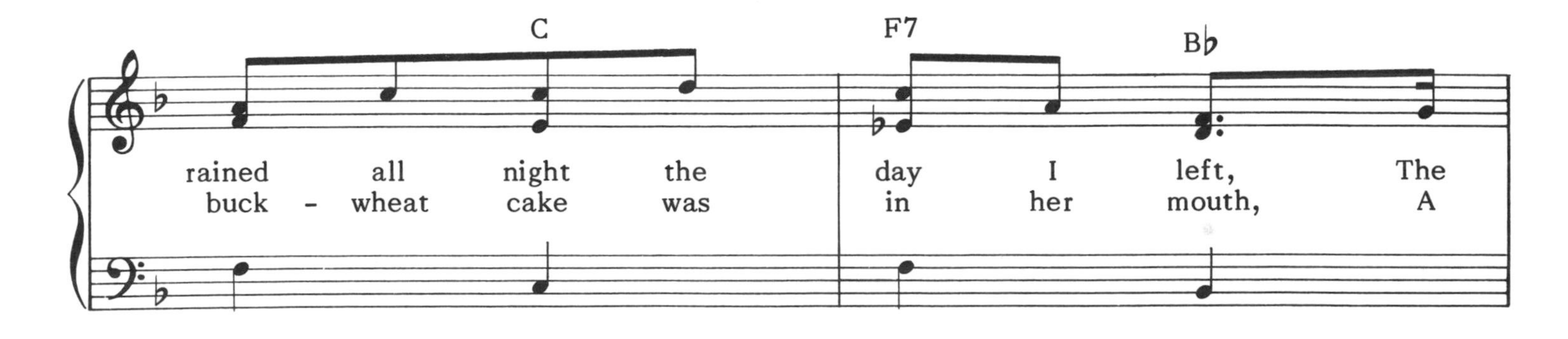

Dm G7 C F C
wea - ther it was dry, The — sun so hot I
tear was in her eye; Says — I, "I'm com - ing
F7 B♭ G9 C7 F
froze to death, Sus - an - na, don't you cry.
from the South, Sus - an - na, don't you cry.
Chorus
B♭ C/B♭ F G7
Oh, Sus - an - na, Oh don't you cry for
C F C F7 B♭
me; I — come from Al - a - bam - a with a
G9 C7 1 F 2 F
ban - jo on my knee. knee.

ON ILKLEY MOOR BAHT'AT

TRADITIONAL

2. Thou's been a-courtin' Mary Jane...

3. Thou'll go and get thee death o'cold...

4. Then we shall have to bury thee...

5. Then t'worms'll come and eat thee up...

6. Then t'ducks'll come and eat up t'worms...

7. Then we shall go and eat up t'ducks...

8. Then we shall all have eaten thee...

9. That's where we gets us own back...

ON MOTHER KELLY'S DOORSTEP

Words and Music
by GEO. A STEVEN

C/G Am Dm G7 C Dm7 E♭° C
Nel-ly was the smartest down our al-ley. On Moth-er Kel-ly's
Gm C7 F E
door - step, I'm wondering now If little gal
C7 F C F Gm C7
Nel - ly re-mem-bers Joe, her beau, And does she
Dm E7 Am7 D7
love me like she used to, On Moth-er Kel-ly's
Gm C7 F
door - step, down Par-a-dise Row.

PACK UP YOUR TROUBLES IN YOUR OLD KIT BAG

Words and Music by
GEORGE ASAF and FELIX POWELL

A
D
A7
D7
Smile, boys that's the style.
G
D
G7
What's the use of wor-ry-ing? It
Am
D
G
Em
A
D7
nev - cr was worth - while, so
G
Dm
E7
Am
Pack up your trou-bles in your old kit - bag And
G/D
D7
G
smile, smile, smile.

POLLY-WOLLY-DOODLE

TRADITIONAL

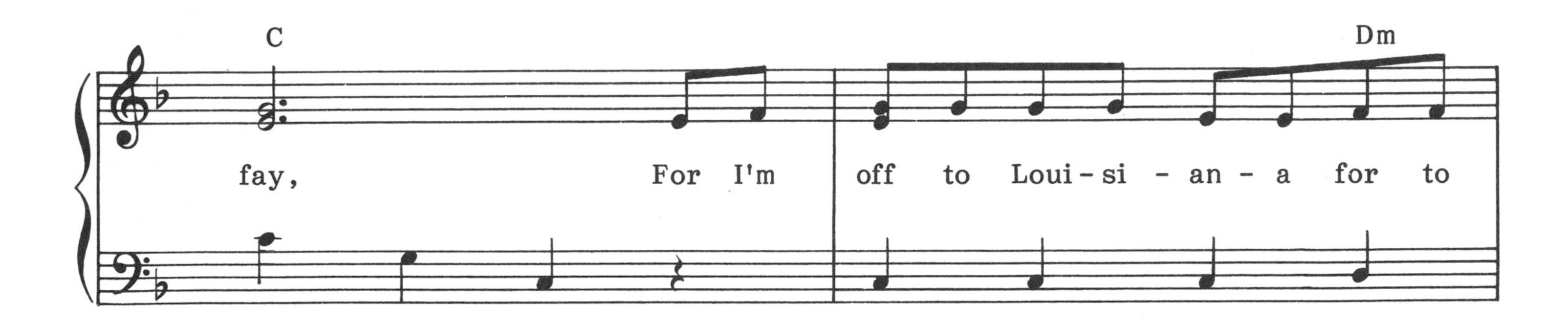

2. Oh my Sal she am a maiden fair,
Sing Polly wolly doodle all the day;
With curly eyes and laughing hair,
Sing Polly wolly doodle all the day.
Chorus

3. A grasshopper sitting on a railroad track,
Sing Polly wolly doodle all the day;
A picking his teeth with a carpet tack,
Sing Polly wolly doodle all the day.
Chorus

ROLL OUT THE BARREL

Words and Music by LEW BROWN,
V A TIMM and T VEJVODA

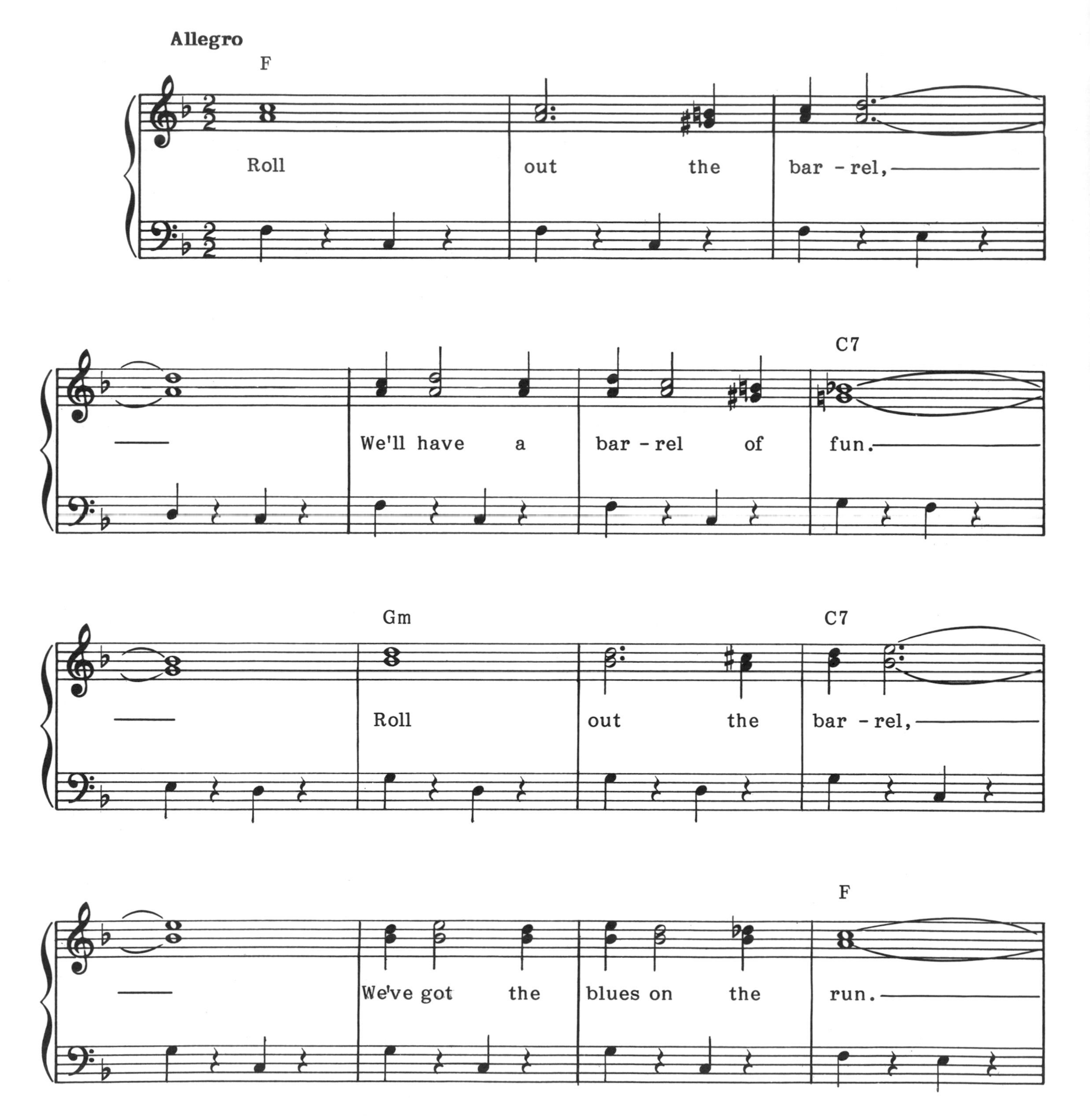

Zing!
Boom! Ta -
rar - rel!
Ring out a
song of good
F7
B♭
D7
cheer.
Gm7
Now's the time to
E7
F
roll the
bar - rel,
For the
G7
C7
F
B♭
F
gang's
all
here.

RULE BRITANNIA

TRADITIONAL

2. The nations not so blest as thee,
   Must in their turn to tyrants bend,
   Must in their turn, must in their turn to tyrants bend.
   While thou shalt flourish, shalt flourish great and free,
   And to the weak protection lend.
   Chorus

3. The Muses, still with freedom found,
   Shall to thy happy coast repair;
   Shall to thy happy coast, thy happy coast repair,
   Blest Isle! With beauty, with matchless beauty crown'd,
   And manly hearts to guard the fair.
   Chorus

SALLY

Words and Music by W E HAINES,
HARRY LEON and L TOWERS

A♭7
When skies are blue you're be - guil - ing,
C/G
C
A♭7
When they are grey you're still smil - ing,
C/G
Am7
Dm9
G7sus
smil - ing,
C
E7
F
Fm
Sal - ly, Sal - ly, pride of our al - ley, You're
C/G
A♭
Dm7
G7
A♭7
C
more than the whole world to me.

SHE'LL BE COMING ROUND THE MOUNTAIN

TRADITIONAL

2. She'll be wearing pink pyjamas when she comes...
Chorus

3. She'll be driving six white horses when she comes...
Chorus

4. Oh, we'll all go to meet her when she comes...
Chorus

SHE'S A LASSIE FROM LANCASHIRE

Words and Music by C W MURPHY,
DAN LIPTON and JOHN NEAT

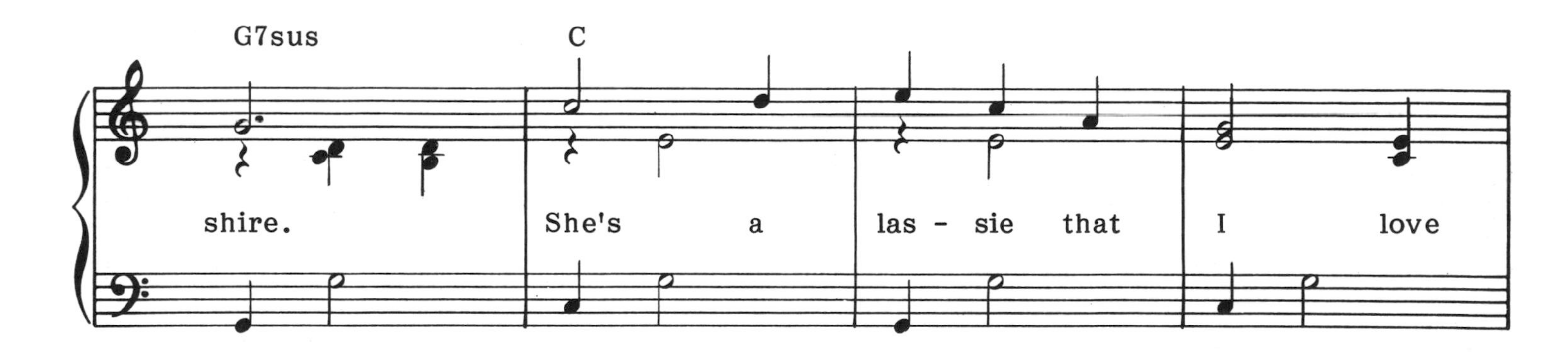

G7
C
Though she dress - es in
clogs and shawl,
G7
She's the pret - ti - est
C
G7sus
C
of them all.
None could be
G7
C
G7
fair - er or rar - er than Sa - rah, My
D7
G7
C
lass from Lan - ca - shire.

SIDE BY SIDE

Words and Music
by HARRY WOODS

C A7sus D7 G7 C E7+
shar-ing our load,— Side by side. Through all kinds of
A9 A
wea - ther, What if the sky should fall? Just as
D7 G9 G0 G7
long as we're to- geth-er, It does-n't mat-ter at all. When they've
C F Fm C F C
all had their quarrels and part - ed, We'll be the same as we start - ed, Just
F C A7sus D7 G7 C
travel-ling a-long,— sing-ing a song,— Side by side.

STAR SPANGLED BANNER

Words and Music by
J SMITH and F S KEY

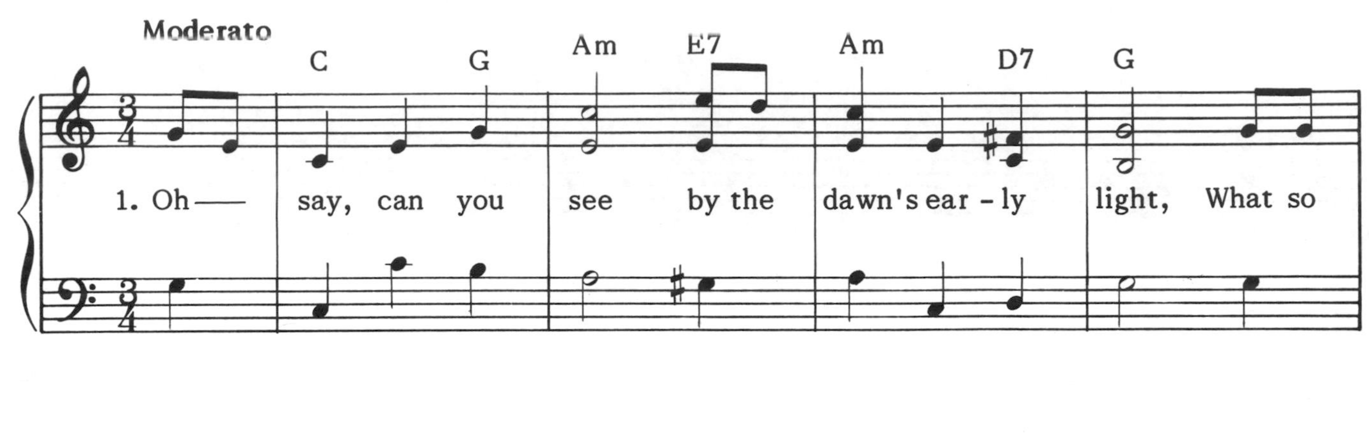

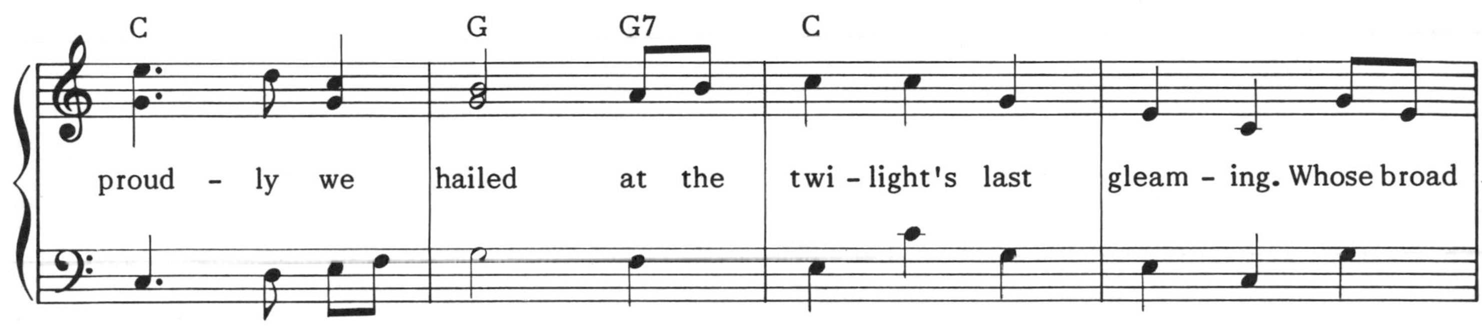

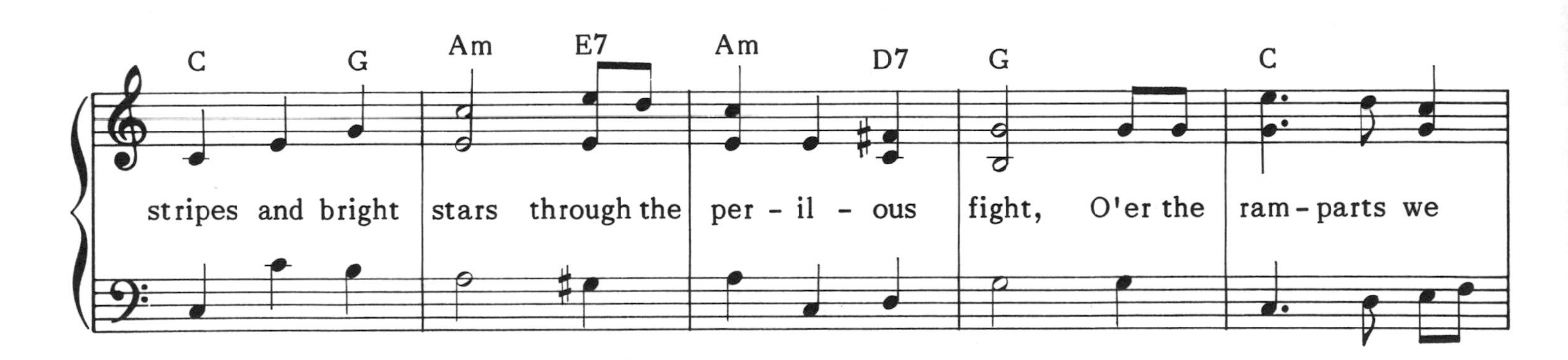

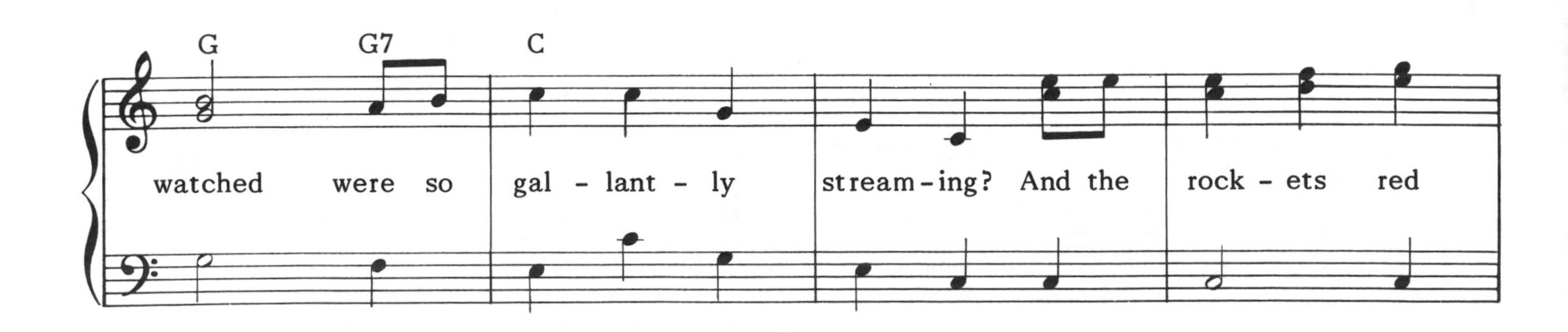

2. On the shore dimly seen through the mists of the deep,
Where the foe's haughty host in dread silence reposes,
What is that which the breeze o'er the towering steep,
As it fitfully blows, half conceals, half discloses?
Now it catches the gleam of the morning's first beam,
Its full glory reflected now shines in the stream.
'Tis the Star-Spangled Banner, oh long may it wave
O'er the land of the free, and the home of the brave.

3. Oh, thus be it ever when free men shall stand
Between their loved homes and war's desolation;
Blest with victory and peace, may the Heaven-rescued land,
Praise the Power that hath made and preserved us a nation!
Then conquer we must, when our cause it is just,
And this is our motto, "In God is our Trust."
And the Star-Spangled Banner in triumph doth wave
O'er the land of the free, and the home of the brave.

SHOW ME THE WAY TO GO HOME

Words and Music
by IRVING KING

THE HONEYSUCKLE AND THE BEE

Words by W PENN
Music by A H FITZ

SWEET GENEVIEVE

TRADITIONAL

G
D7
C
B
ev - ery dream, My wak - ing thoughts are full of thee; Thy
no re - gret, What e'er the years may bring to me; I
B7
Em
Em7
Am
glance is in the star - ry beam That falls a - long the
bless the hour when first we met, The hour that gave me
B
D7
Chorus
G
D
sum - mer sea.—
love and thee.—
Oh, Gen - e-vieve, sweet Gen - e-vieve, The
D7
G
3
G7
days may come, the days — may go, But still the hands of
C
Cm
G/D
D7
G
mem - 'ry weave, The bliss - ful dreams of long a - go.

TAKE ME BACK TO DEAR OLD BLIGHTY

Words and Music by A J MILLS,
FRED GODFREY and BENNETT SCOTT

F C7 F7
Bir - ming - ham, well I don't care.
B♭ E♭m6 B♭
I should love to see my best girl
B♭7 E♭6 G0 G♭7
Cud-dle-ing up a - gain we soon should be, So,
B♭/F E♭ B♭/F C C7
tid-dle-y id-dle-y - igh - ty, hur-ry me home to Bligh - ty,
F7 B♭
Bligh - ty is the place for me.
sfz

THE ANNIVERSARY WALTZ

Words and Music by
AL DUBIN and DAVE FRANKLIN

G9+ C6 C#0 Dm7 G7 C7
dream come true. Let this be the
an - them to our fu - ture years, To
F
A7 D9 G7+
mil - lions of smiles and a few lit - tle tears.
C Asus A
May I al - ways list - en to the
D7 G7 C
An - ni - ver - sa - ry Waltz with you.

THE CHESTNUT TREE ('Neath The Spreading Chestnut Tree)

Words by HAMILTON KENNEDY and TOMMIE CONNOR
Music by JIMMY KENNEDY

Csus9 C7 F F#0 C/G Am7 A A-
buts," She said, "I love you," and the
G/D D7 Gsus G7 C
black - smith shout - ed, "Chest - nuts!" Un - derneath the spread - ing
F C/G Am Em F6 G C
chest - nut tree There she said she'd mar - ry me,
F Em F G C
Now you ought to see our fam - i - ly
F C F C/G G7 C
'Neath the spread - ing chest - nut tree.

THE DRUNKEN SAILOR

TRADITIONAL

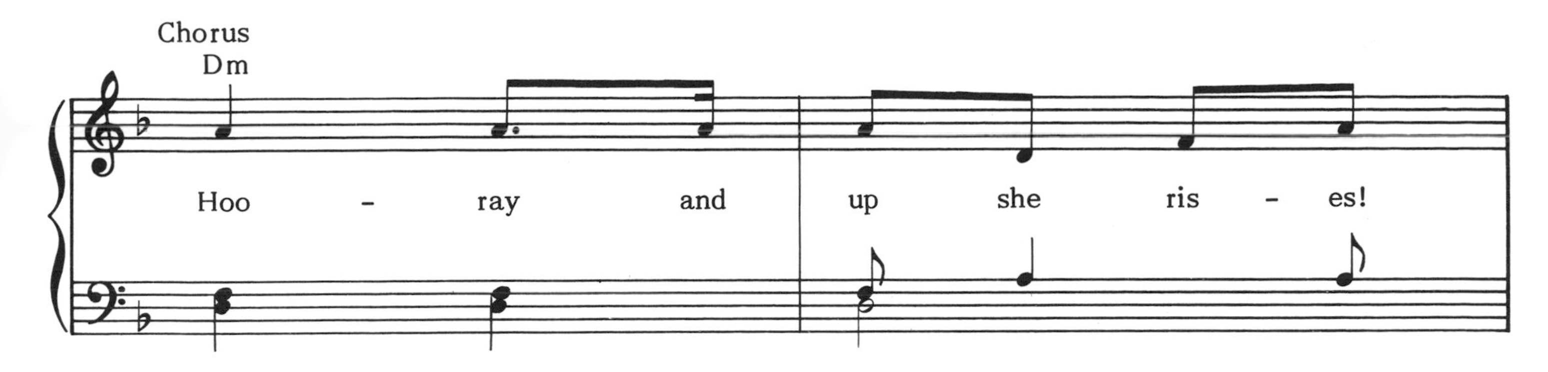

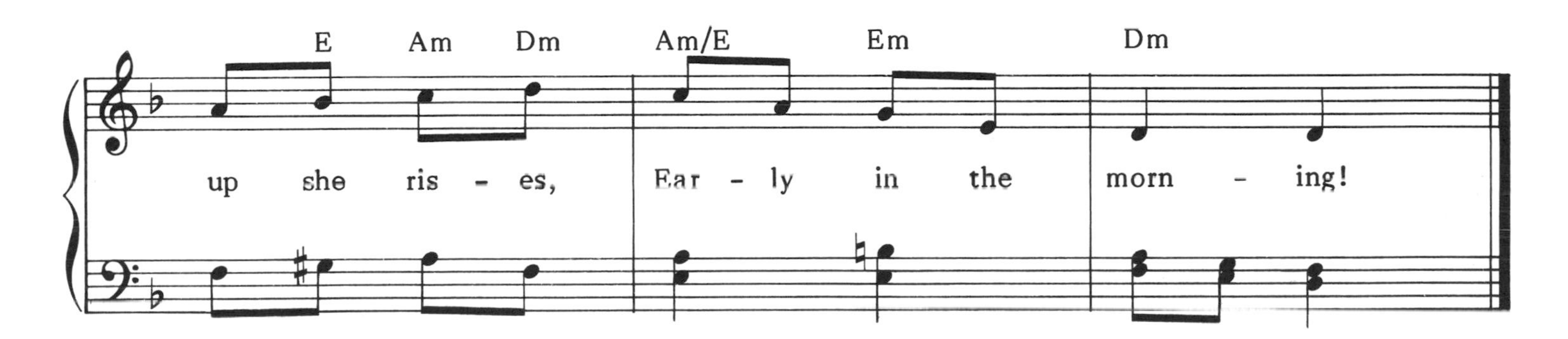

2. Put him in the long boat till he's sober . . .

CHORUS

3. Give him a taste of the bosun's rope end . . .

CHORUS

4. Give him a dose of salt and water . . .

CHORUS

5. Put on his back a mustard plaster . . .

CHORUS

6. That's what to do with a drunken sailor . . .

CHORUS

THE HAPPY WANDERER

Words by ANTONIA RIDGE
Music by FRIEDR W MOLLER

Chorus
B♭
F7
back.
sky.
Val - de
ri,
val - de
B♭
F7
ra,
Val - de
ri,
val - de
B♭
B⁰
ha ha ha ha
ha ha Val - de
F7
B♭
B♭7
Gm
G7
ri,
Val - de
ra,
My
Be -
Cm7
B♭/F
F7
B♭
knap - sack
on my
back.
- neath God's
clear blue
sky.

THE LORD'S MY SHEPHERD

TRADITIONAL

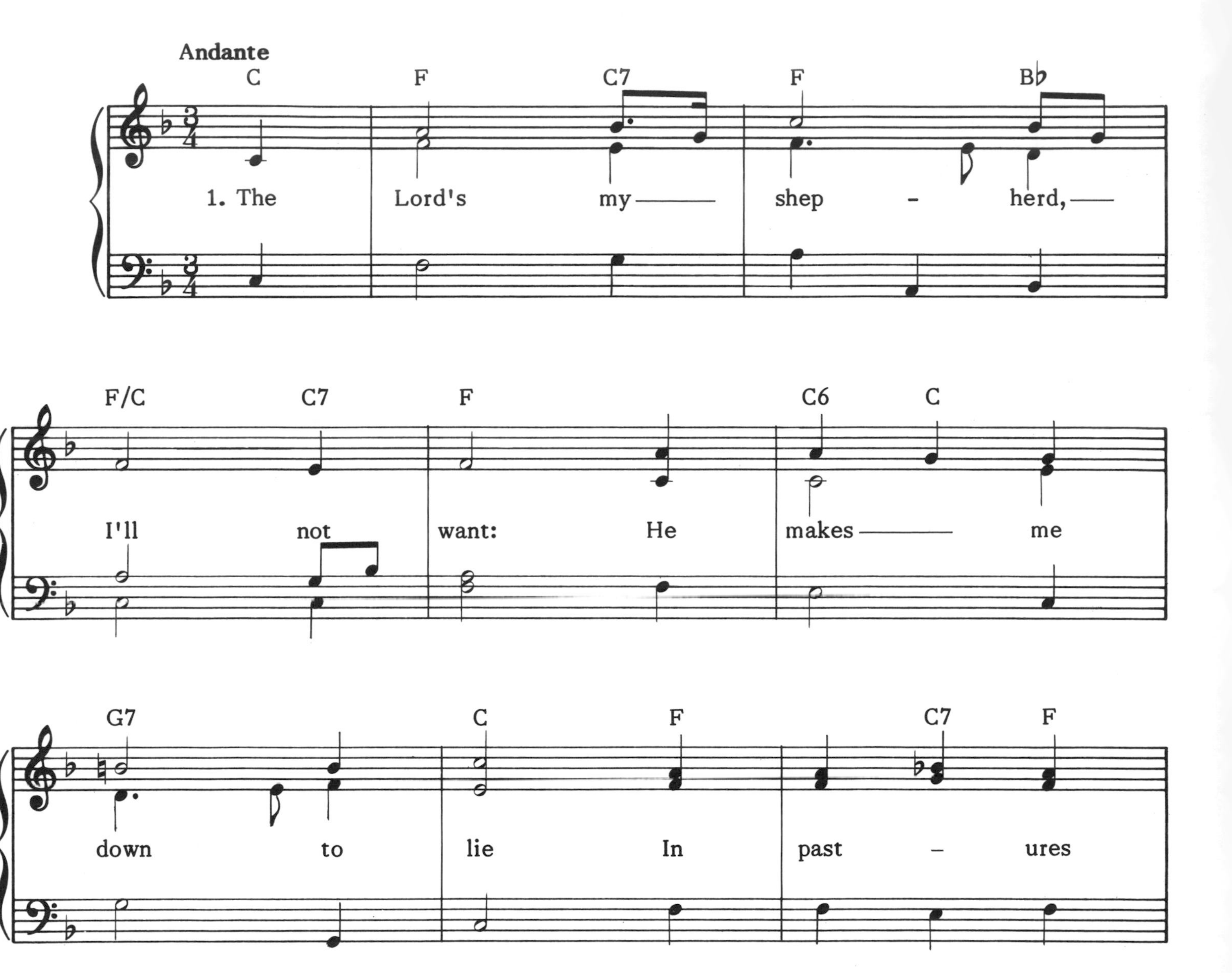

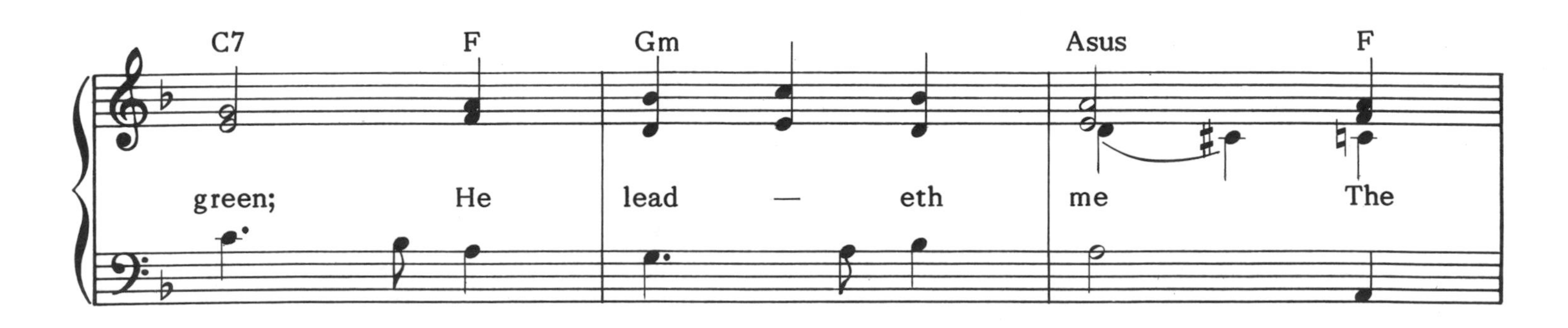

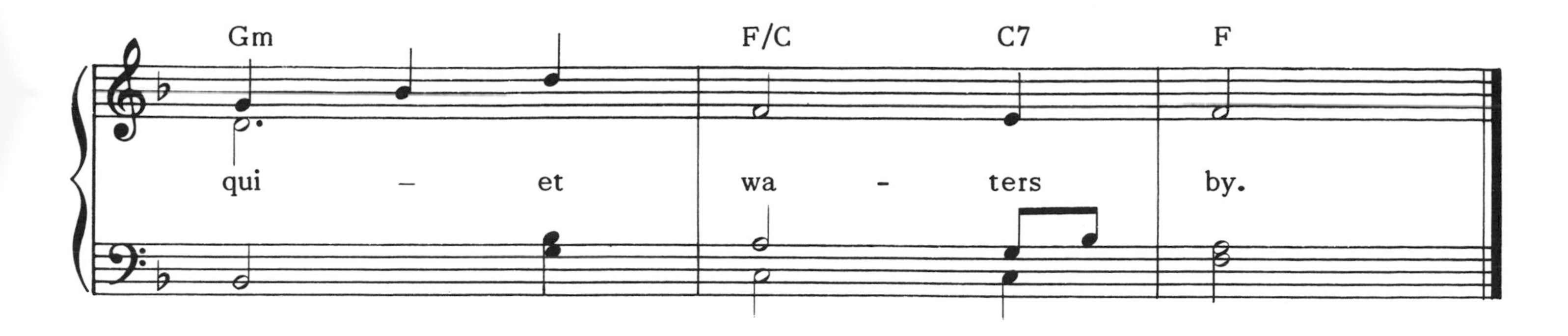

2. My soul He doth restore again;
And me to walk doth make
Within the path of righteousness,
E'en for his own names sake.

3. Yea, though I walk through death's dark vale,
Yet will I fear none ill:
For Thou art with me; and Thy rod
And staff me comfort still.

4. My table Thou hast furnished
In presence of my foes;
My head Thou dost with oil anoint,
And my cup overflows.

5. Goodness and mercy all my life
Shall surely follow me;
And in God's house for evermore
My dwelling-place shall be.

THE MOUNTAINS OF MOURNE

Words and Music by
PERCY FRENCH and HOUSTON COLLISSON

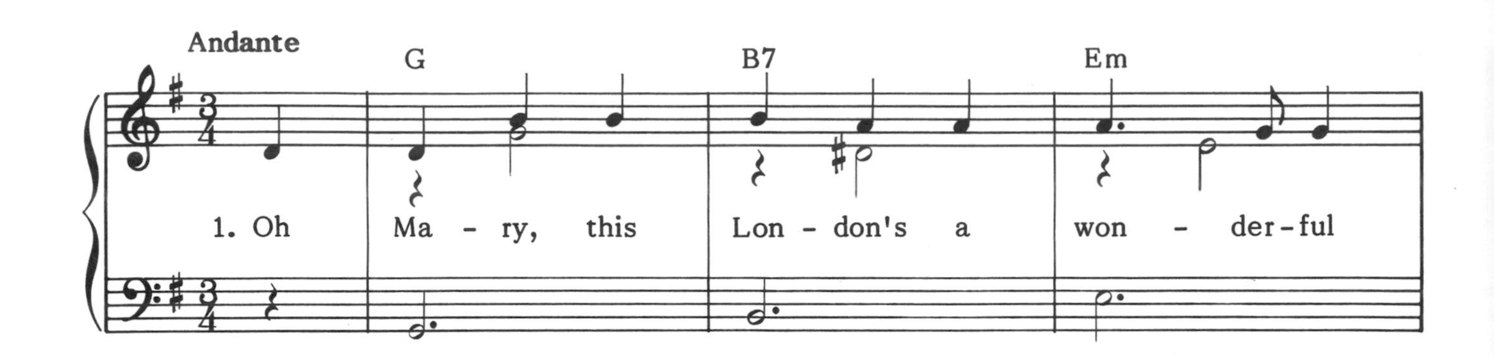

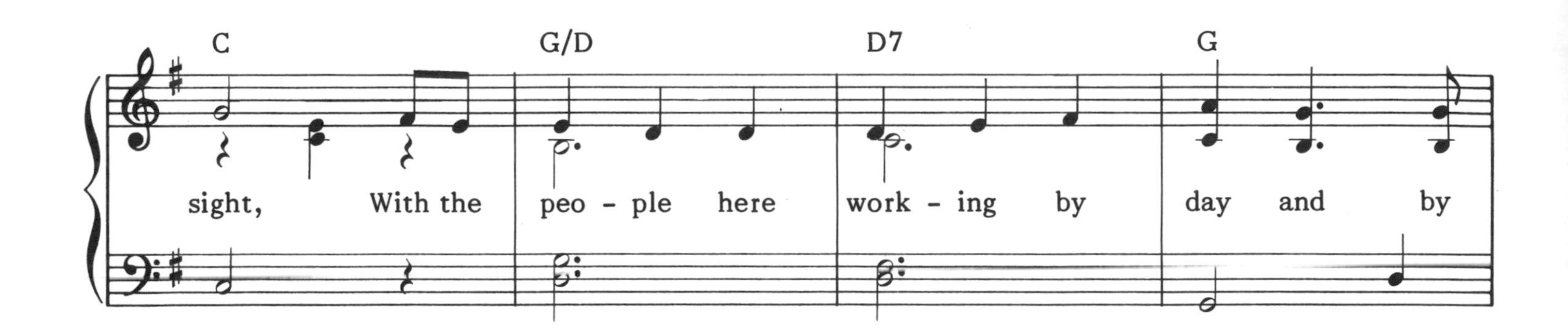

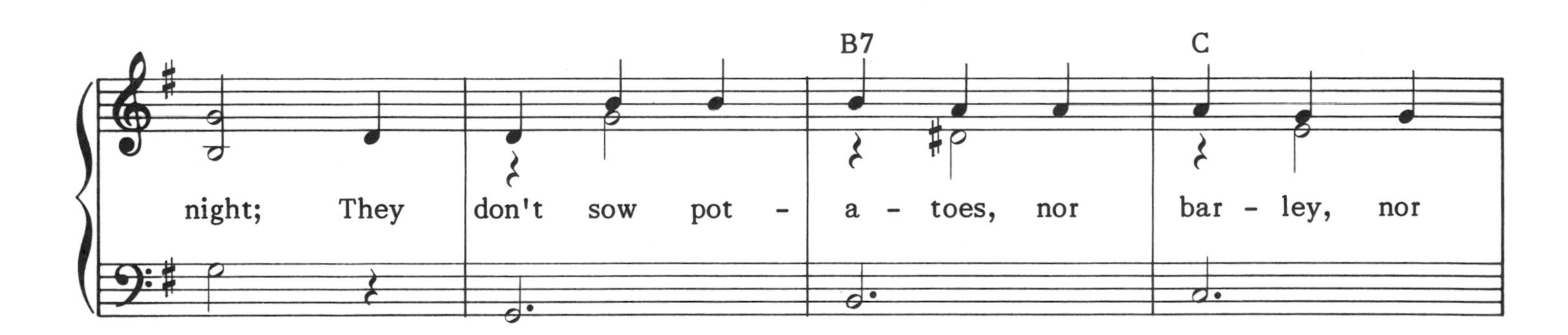

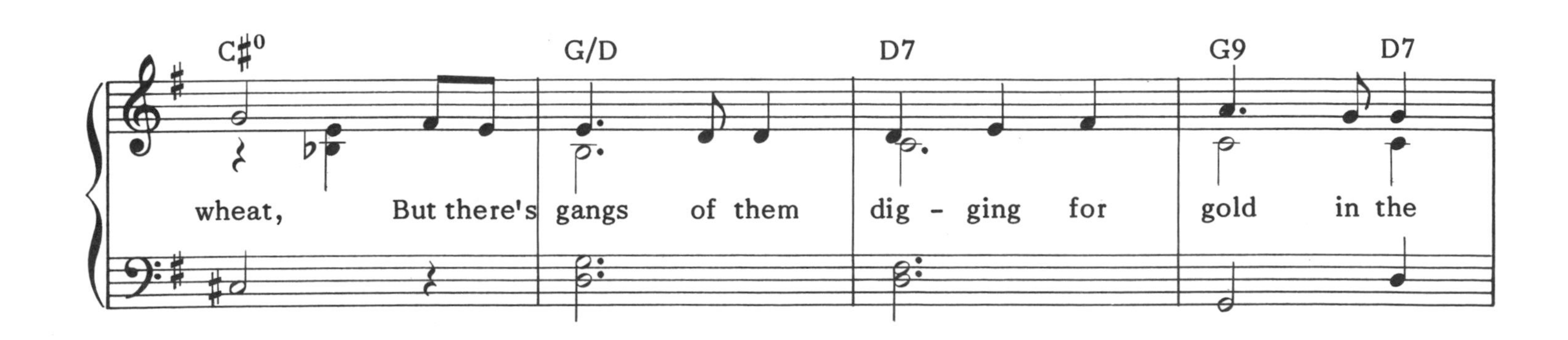

2. There's beautiful girls here, oh, never mind,
With beautiful shapes nature never designed,
And lovely complexions all roses and cream,
But O'Loughlin remarked with regard to the same:
That if at those roses you venture to sip
The colours might all come away on your lip,
So I'll wait for the wild rose that's waiting for me
Where the Mountains o' Mourne sweep down to the sea.

THE OLD FOLKS AT HOME

Words and Music
by STEPHEN C FOSTER

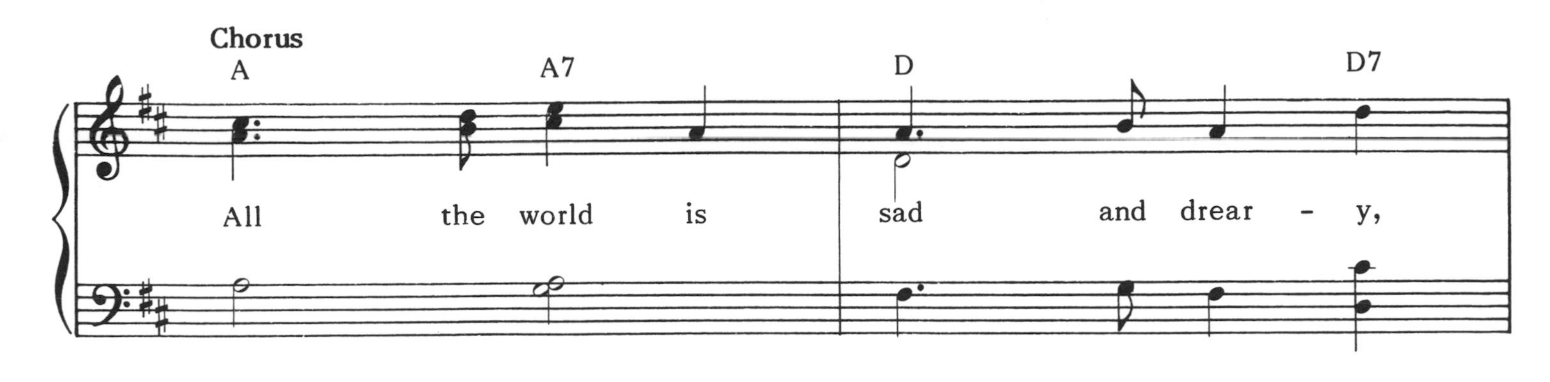

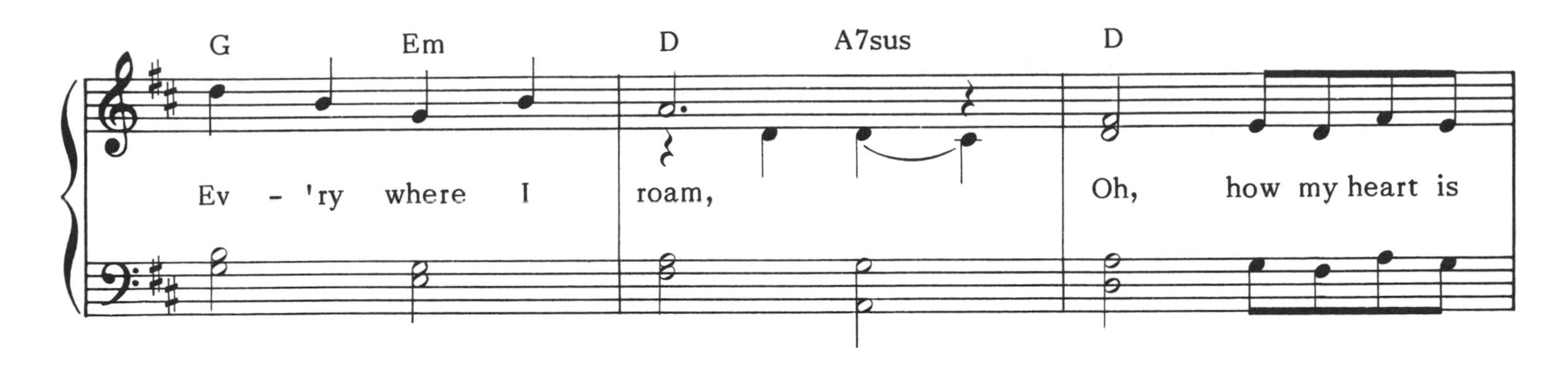

2. All round the little farm I wandered,
When I was young;
Then many happy days I squandered,
Many the song I sung.
When I was playing with my brother,
Happy was I;
Oh! take me to my kind old mother,
There let me live and die.

Chorus

THE QUARTERMASTER STORE

TRADITIONAL

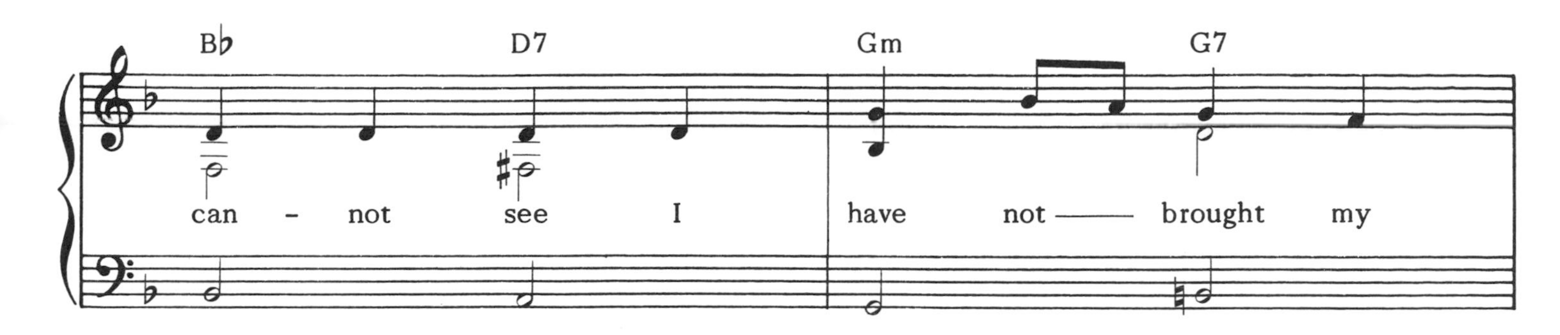

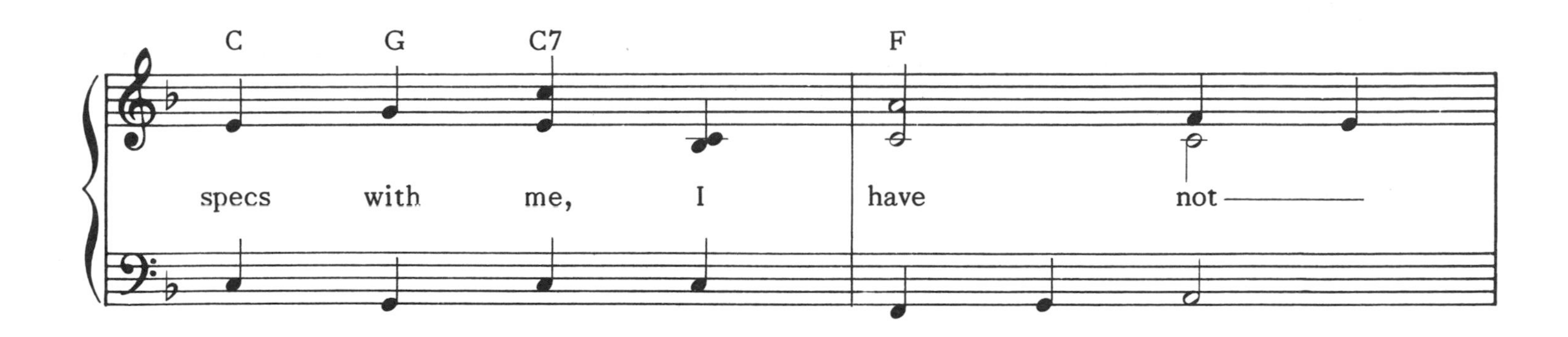

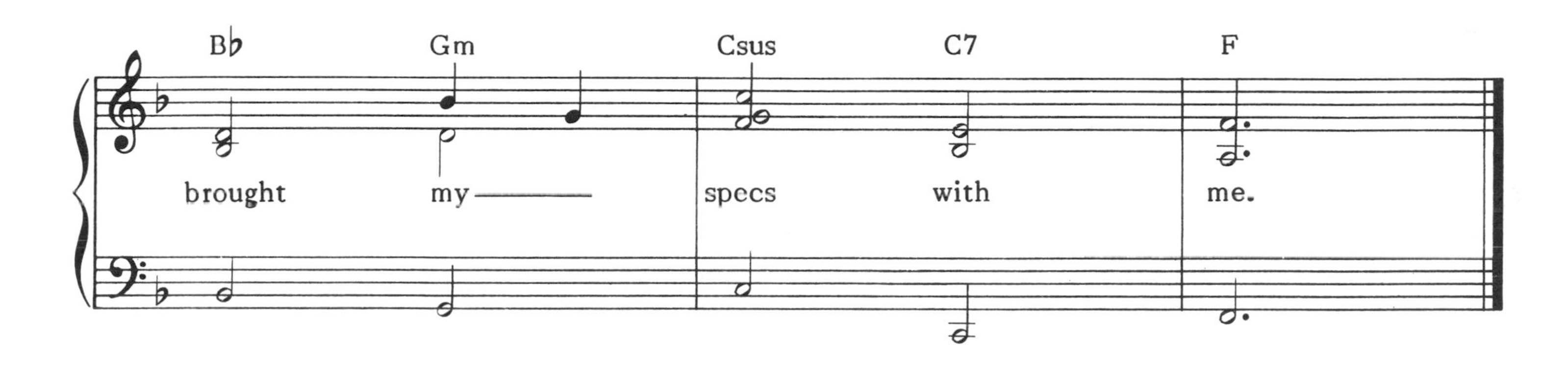

2. There was steak, steak, tough as cattle cake,
   In the stores, in the stores.
   There was steak, steak, to give you belly ache,
   In the Quartermaster's stores.

   Chorus

3. There was bread, bread, harder than your head,
   In the stores, in the stores.
   There was bread, bread, just like lumps of lead,
   In the Quartermaster's stores.

   Chorus

THE RED FLAG

TRADITIONAL

2. It waved about our infant might,
When all ahead seemed dark as night;
It witnessed many a deed and vow;
We must not change its colour now.

Chorus

3. It well recalls the triumphs past,
It gives the hope of peace at last;
The banner bright, the symbol plain,
Of human right and human gain.

Chorus

4. It suits today the weak and base,
Whose minds are fixed on self and place;
To cringe before the rich man's frown,
And haul the sacred emblem down.

Chorus

5. With heads uncovered swear we all,
To bear it onward till we fall;
Come dungeon dark or gallows grim,
This song shall be our parting hymn.

Chorus

THERE IS A TAVERN IN THE TOWN

TRADITIONAL

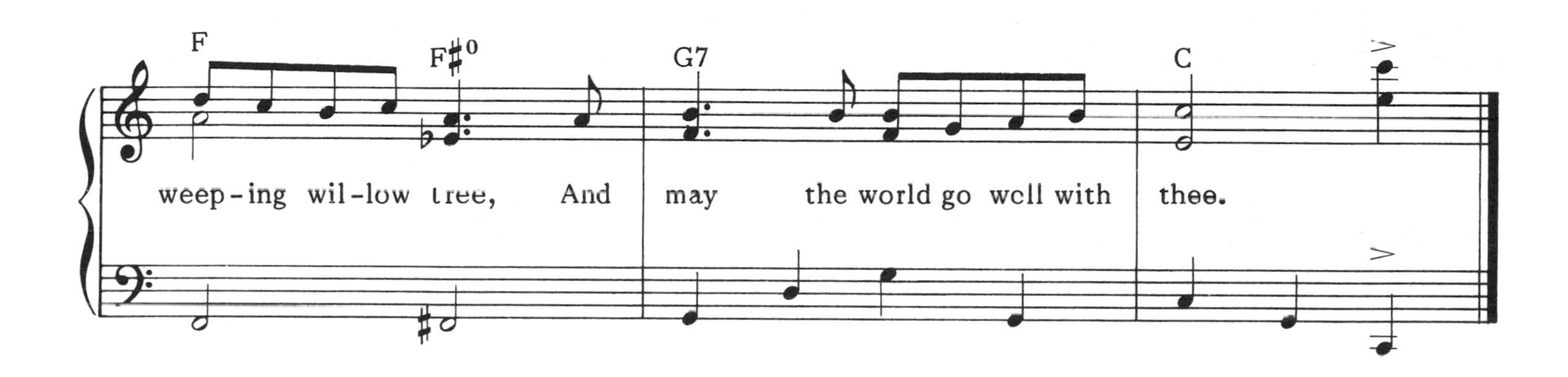

2. He left me for a damsel dark, damsel dark,
Each Friday night they used to spark, used to spark,
And now my love once true to me,
Takes that dark damsel on his knee.

Chorus

3. Oh, dig my grave both wide and deep, wide and deep,
Put tombstones at my head and feet, head and feet,
And on my breast carve a turtle dove,
To signify I died of love.

Chorus

THERE'S SOMETHING ABOUT A SOLDIER

Words and Music
by NOEL GAY

B♭ B♭0 B♭
May be a sim - ple priv - ate of the line, line, line. But there's
B♭
some-thing a-bout his bear - ing, Something in what he's wear - ing,
G7 Cm G7 Cm
Some-thing a-bout his but tons all a - shine, shine, shine. Oh, a
E♭m6 B♭/F C7
mil - it - a - ry chest seems to suit the lad - ies best, There's
B♭/F F7 B♭
some-thing a-bout a sold - ier that is fine, fine, fine.

THE ROSE OF TRALEE

Words by C M SPENCER
Music by C W GLOVER

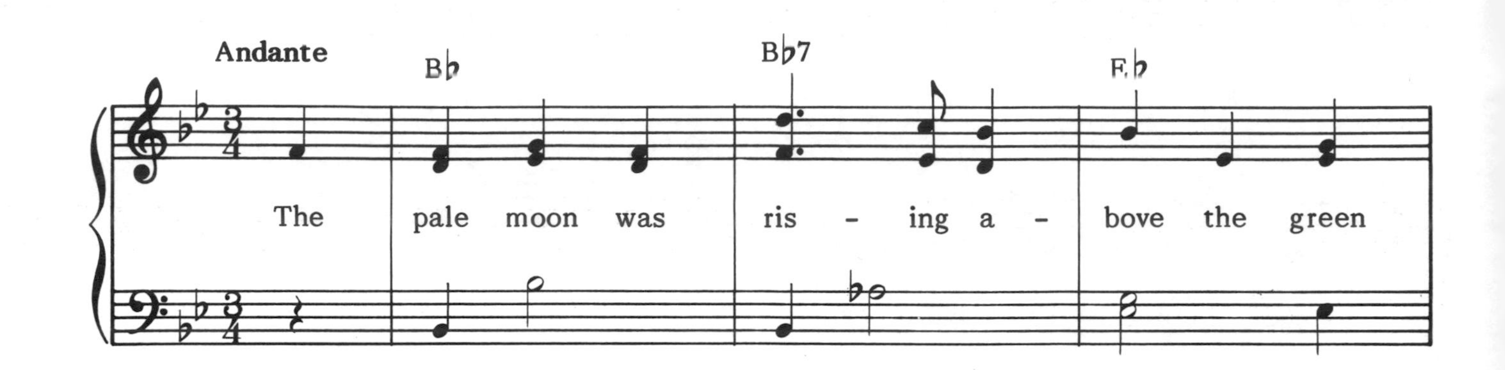

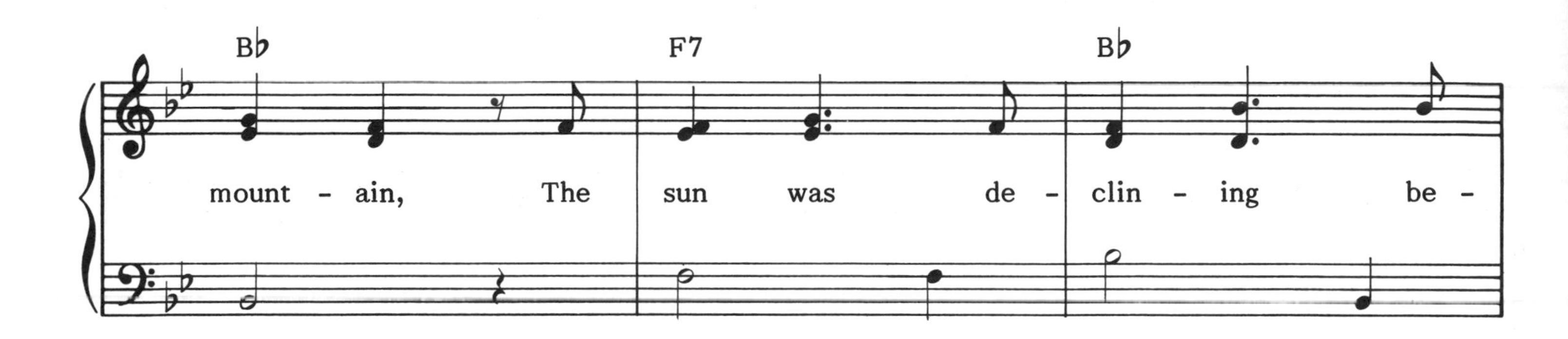

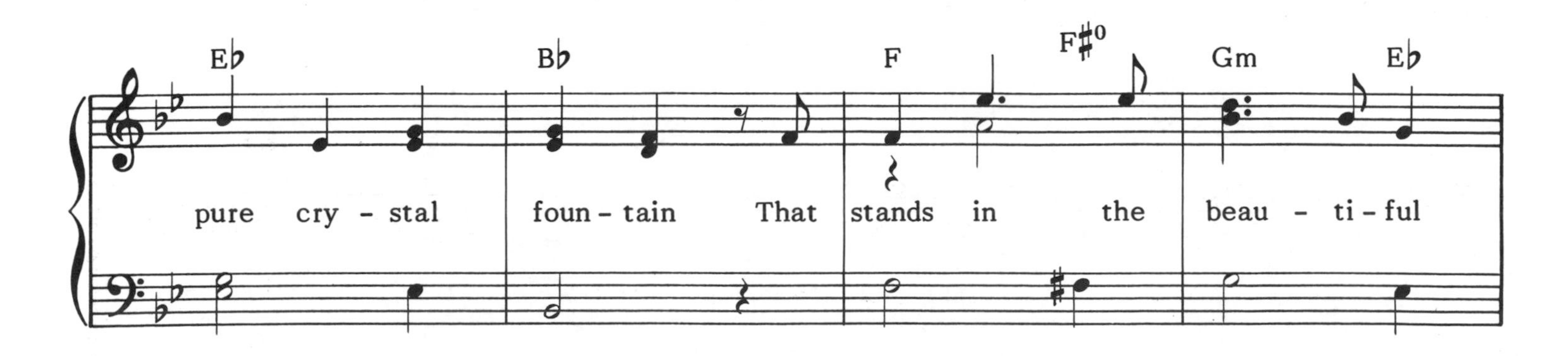

B♭/F F7 B♭ D7 Gm
vale of Tra - lee. She was love - ly and fair as the
A7 D Gm Cm
rose of the summer, Yet 'twas not her
D7 Gm Cm D7 Gm F7 B♭
beau - ty a - lone that won me. Oh, no, 'twas the
B♭7 E♭ B♭
truth in her eye ev - er dawn - ing, That
F7 B♭ E♭ B♭/F F7 B♭
made me love Ma - ry, the rose of Tra - lee.

TIP-TOE THRO' THE TULIPS WITH ME

Words by AL DUBIN
Music by JOE BURKE

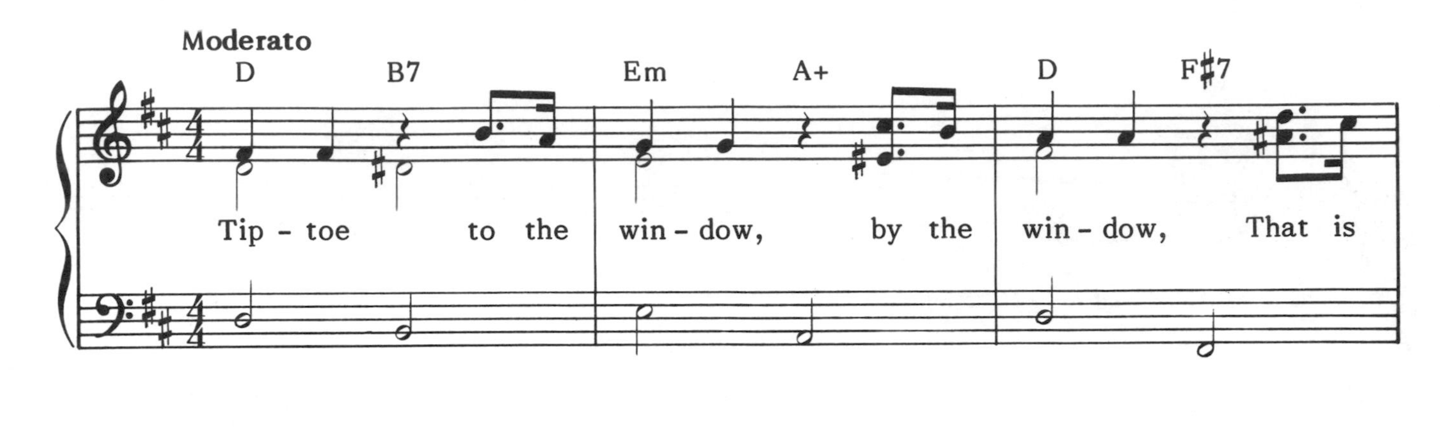

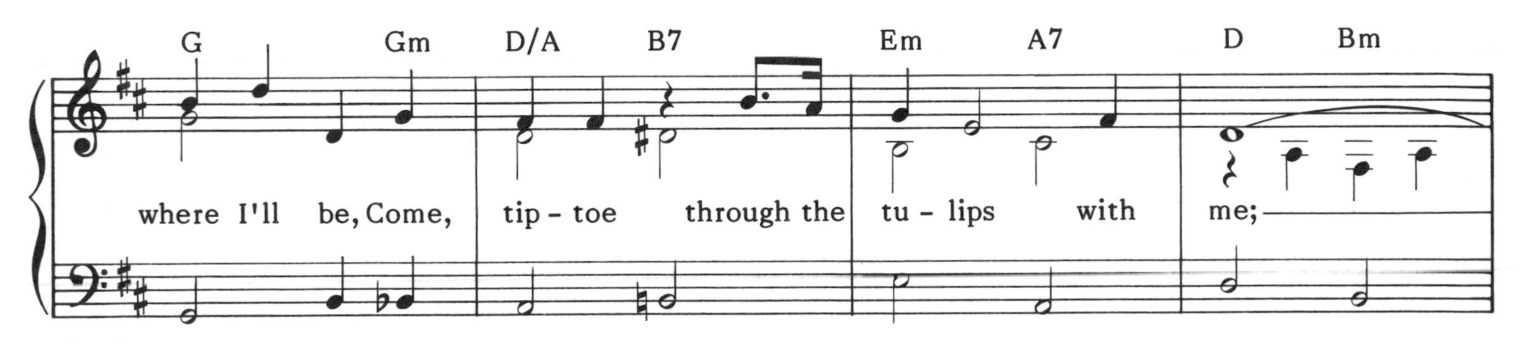

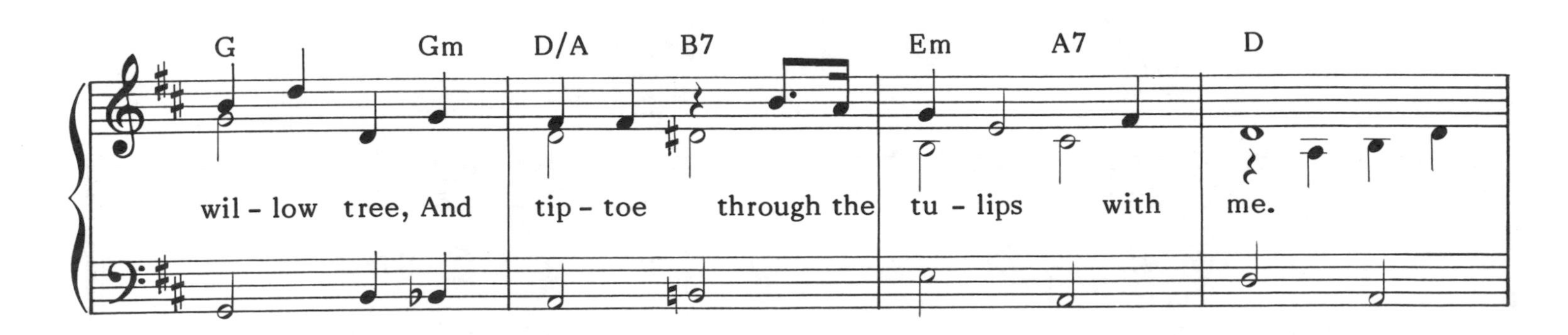

G6 F0 F♯m E0 B7
Knee deep in flow - ers we'll stray,
C♯7 F♯m F0 A7
We'll keep the show - ers a - way;
B E9 A7 D B7 Em A+
And if I kiss you in the gar - den, In the
D F♯7 G Gm D/A B7
moon - light, Will you par - don me, Come, tip - toe through the
Em A7 D Gm D
tu - lips with me.
R.H.
3

UNDERNEATH THE ARCHES

Words and Music by BUD FLANAGAN
(Additional Words by REG CONNELLY)

F7 Bb
Her-ald-ing the dawn. Sleep-ing when it's rain - ing
C7 F7
and sleep-ing when it's fine, I hear the trains rat - tling
A7-5 D Gm D0 D7 G7+ G7
by a - bove, Pavement is my pil - low,
Gm7 C7
no mat-ter where I stray, Un-derneath the
Cm7 Ebm F7 Bb
arch - es, I dream my dreams a - way.

WALTZING MATILDA

Words by A B PATERSON
Music by MARIE COWAN

F/C C D7 Gm C7 F Asus A7
You'll come a-waltz - ing Ma - til - da with me." And he sang as he watched and
Dm7 B♭ B⁰ F/C Dm7 Gm
wait - ed till his bill - y boiled, "You'll come a - waltz - ing Ma -
Csus C7 F
Fine
F C7 Dm7 B♭ F
- til - da with me."
2. Down came a jum - buck to drink at the bill - a - bong,
Gm C7 F Csus A7
Up jumped a swag - man and grabbed him with glee, And he sang as he stowed that
Dm7 B♭ F F♯⁰ Gm Csus C7 F
Repeat Chorus
jum - buck in his tuck - er bag, "You'll come a - waltz - ing Ma - til - da with me."

WE'LL KEEP A WELCOME

Words by LYN JOSHUA and JAMES HARPER
Music by MAI JONES

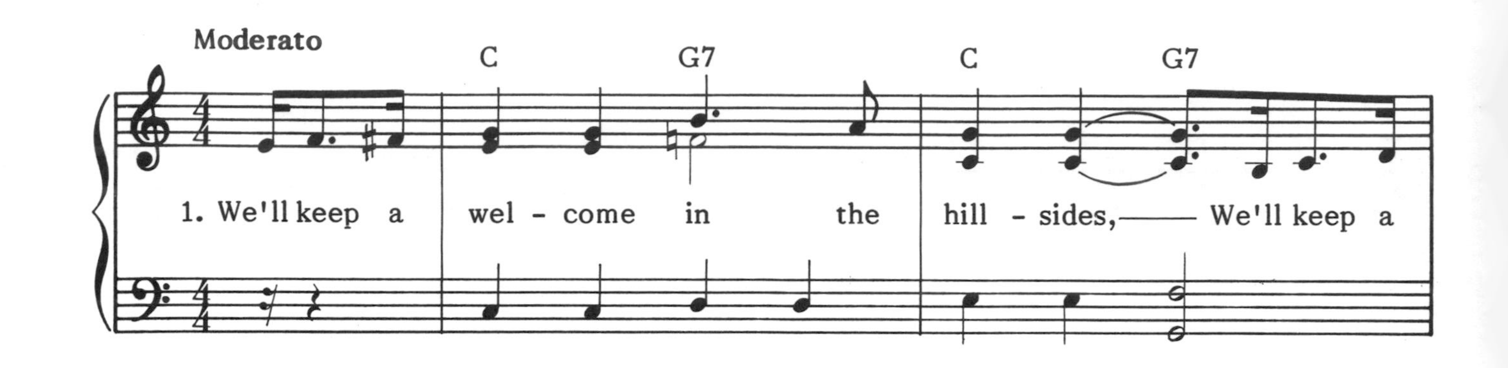

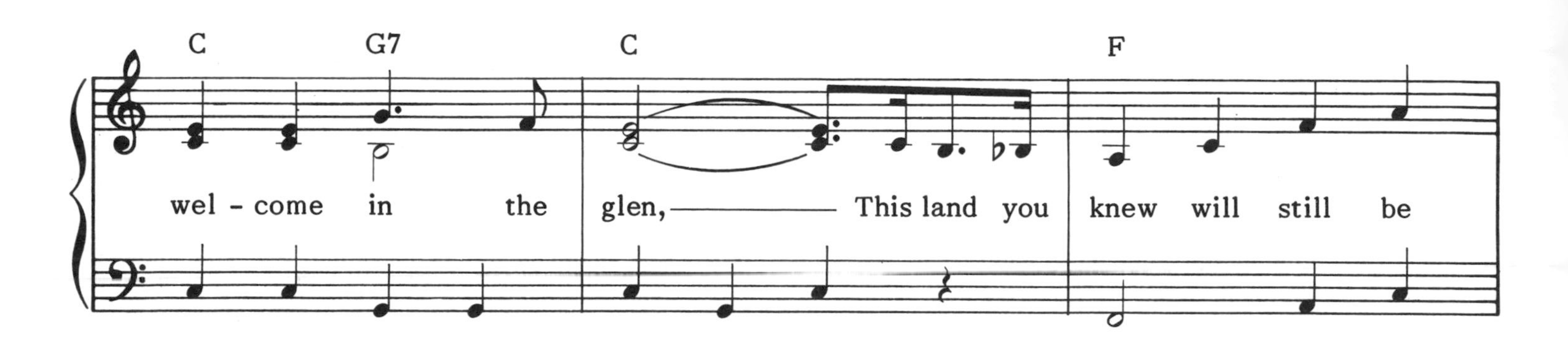

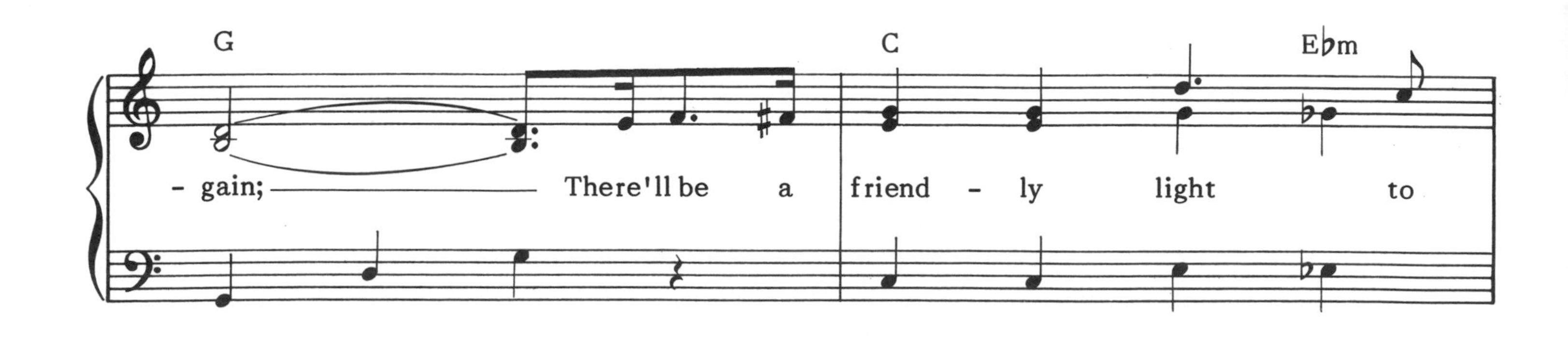

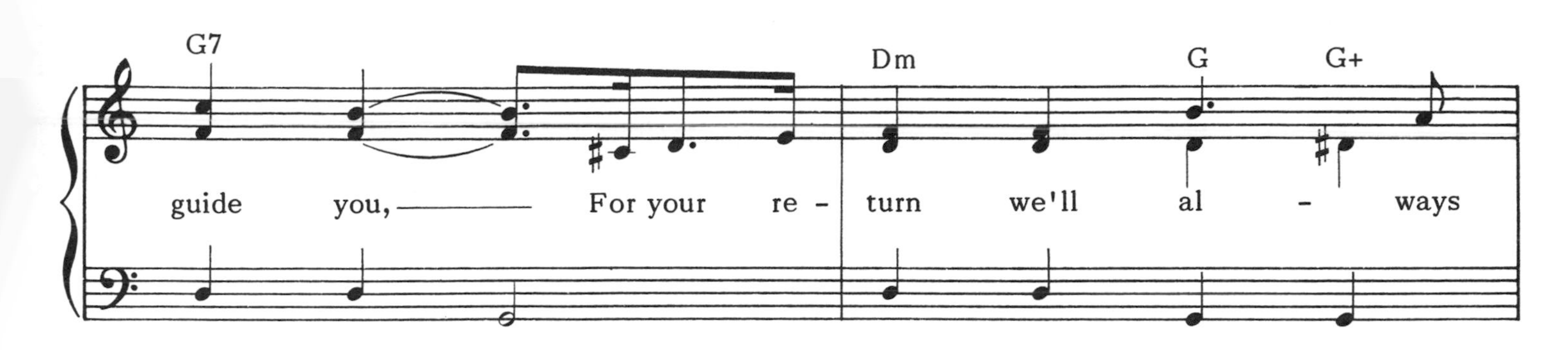

2. We'll keep a welcome in the hillsides,
We'll keep a welcome in the vales,
This land you knew will still be singing
When you come home again to Wales.
This land of song will keep a welcome,
And with a love that never fails,
We'll kiss away each hour of Hiraeth
When you come home again to Wales.
We'll kiss away each hour of Hiraeth
When you come home again to Wales.

(WE'RE GONNA HANG OUT) THE WASHING ON THE SIEGFRIED LINE

Words and Music by
JIMMY KENNEDY and MICHAEL CARR

B♭
B♭7
day is here. Whe - ther the
E♭
C9
wea - ther may be wet or fine We'll just rub a - long
F7
B♭
with - out a care. We're going to hang out the
B♭7
G7
wash - ing on the Sieg - fried Line, If the
Cm
B♭/F
F7
B♭
Sieg - fried Line's still there.

WHEN YOU'RE SMILING

Words and Music by MARK FISHER,
JOE GOODWIN and LARRY SHAY

B♭
B♭7
through; But when you're cry - ing you
E♭
C7
bring on the rain, So stop your sigh - ing,
F
F0
F7
be hap - py a - gain; Keep on
B♭
G7
smil - ing, 'cause when you're smil - ing, The
Cm
F7
B♭
whole world smiles with you.

YOU ARE MY SUNSHINE

Words and Music by
JIMMY DAVIS and CHARLES MITCHELL

Chorus
C7
F
Fm
C7 No Chord
F
then I cried.
breath your name.
You are my sun - shine,
My on - ly sun - shine,
F7
You make me
B♭
C7
F
F7
hap - py When skies are grey. You'll nev - er
B♭
C7
F
Dm
B♭m
know, dear, How much I love you; Please don't
F/C
C7
F
take my sun-shine a - way.

YOURS

Words by JACK SHERR
Music by GONZALO ROIG

Em7 A7 D G/D D D0
Yours in the grey of De -
G/D D D7 B7
- cem - ber Here or on far dis - tant
Em F0
shores; I've nev - er loved an - y -
D7 B7 Em Gm
- one the way I love you, How could I? When I was
D/A A7 D
born to be just yours?

YOU MADE ME LOVE YOU (I Didn't Want To Do It)

Words by JOE McCARTHY
Music by JAMES V MONACO

A7
A♭
A7
A-9
A7
You made me hap - py some - times,
D7
Am7
Fm7 D7
you made me glad,
But there were
times, dear, you
G7
G♭7
G7
made me feel so bad.
C
E♭0
You made me sigh for, I
Dm7
Fm6
G7
did - n't want to tell you, I
Dm7
Fm6
G7
did - n't want to tell you,

Printed in Great Britain by Hobbs the Printers Ltd, Totton, Hampshire 1/98